Willi Whizkas

Tall Tales and Lost Lives!

Paws & Claws

Zymurgy
Publishing

A Zymurgy Publishing book

First published in Great Britain by
Zymurgy Publishing in 2005.

A CIP catalogue record for this book is available from the
British Library.

Printed and bound by Bookmarque, U.K.

10 9 8 7 6 5 4 3 2 1

ISBN 1 903506 18 2

Zymurgy Publishing
Newcastle upon Tyne

Contents

Author Details

Jonnie Paws and Carol Claws worked together for the same Staffordshire company for many years before getting married in 1988. They are fortunate that their three cats, Teddie 'The Ginger Flash', Oliver Zinfandal (officially Britain's grumpiest cat) and the new addition Baybee are obsessed with supervising humans and allow them to share their home. They are devoted to their cats, their home is organised around the whims and fancies of their cats.

In 1991 they started to write Willi Whizkas stories together, based upon cats they have known and real cat incidents. Originally written as a private muse, Paws and Claws were encouraged to continue writing by friends who read their work.

Jonnie Paws works as a Quality Auditor for a brand leading adhesive manufacturer in Stoke on Trent, he enjoys walking, travelling and is a good raconteur of corny and risqué jokes

Carol Claws is the Complaint Manager for a national adhesive company, she enjoys travel and presenting programmes for local radio.

1 Willi Whizkas

The day began like most others. Willi Whizkas had spent the night in the kitchen, one of his very favourite places. He was stretched out on the work surface above the freezer where the warmth kept him nice and snug all night. He didn't always stay in; on summer evenings he would find a nice spot under the bushes keeping an eye out for all the twilight activity, especially hedgehogs which snuffled and crashed their way through the garden. One evening he decided to pat one gently with a paw, and got more than he bargained for as his soft pink pads were punctured by the hedgehog's spiky spines.

But last night, for some reason, he had no opportunity to go out. He liked to have adventures in his sleep, dreaming about chasing birds and catching a little grey mouse that lived under the garden shed. In reality, Willi Whizkas had tried to catch him many times, but it didn't matter how low he crouched and slithered his way across the garden, the mouse always seemed to see him coming and darted under the shed out of paw's reach. In his dreams, though, things were different, every once in a while he got his mouse. But just as his fangs were about to close on the hapless mouse something would always wake him up. Today was no exception. The kitchen door opened and his female human came in, saying "good morning Willi," while tickling him under his chin. She put the kettle on, but instead of his breakfast appearing from the cupboard, "horror of horrors," it was his cat basket which came out. Willi Whizkas stood up, arched his back and hissed as the basket was placed next to him. Before he could make his escape, a firm hand grasped him by the scruff of the neck.

"Oh no, you don't you rascal Willi," as he was thrust headlong towards the open basket. Now Willi Whizkas could stretch his paws out, and extend his claws fully, so hooked onto the wickerwork he resembled a furry, snapping, yowling 'X that steadfastly refused to be put into the basket. He clung on for dear life, knowing what the basket meant; the vet! Willi had never forgotten his first visit to the vet: how could he when every time he washed himself he was aware of certain bits were no longer there. Bits he had been rather fond of, actually. Any human who could do that to a nice innocent cat was bad. Very bad indeed. Nearly as bad as a hedgehog.

He once had ingrowing claws, or 'lazy-cat claws' as the vet called them, which would have offended Willi Whizkas if he could understand human-speak, as he considered himself an athletic cat. On another occasion he had stitches put into a very nasty wound after a dust-up with Molly, the cute and appealing black and white stray with a great left hook. The last time he visited the vet was a few weeks ago to have his inoculations, although why they were necessary he had no idea. So he was determined not to get into the basket, the vets meant moggy-misery and humans moaning that they were always welcomed with 'open tills' at the vets. Then the male human came into the kitchen. Two against one! Willi Whizkas was unceremoniously dumped into his basket and carried off, still howling. Standing up in the basket he could just make out the houses that they were passing.

The first house he recognised was where Ginger Tompkins lived, and he caught a glimpse of him sitting in a bedroom window watching the birds in the garden below. Ginger Tompkins was Willi's favourite pal, they'd often get up to mischief and have adventures together.

Willi Whizkas sighed, settled down, and then miaowed pitifully for the entire journey.

The car stopped and Willi Whizkas was taken out, still in his basket. He knew straight away this wasn't the vets, or if it was, the vet had moved into the country. He could see lots of trees and bushes and a large house with outbuildings and cages, and lots and lots of pairs of eyes, all staring at him. Where on earth was he, and who were these other cats looking at him with such interest? Perhaps this was where cats went when they reached a certain age, or when they had been terribly naughty. A door opened and a young girl beckoned Willi's humans in. "Is this Willi Whizkas?" She enquired gently.

"It certainly is! You've got him for a whole two weeks, make sure he gets his favourite food and a good brushing, please," and with that Willi's humans gave him a last "Puss puss," a finger was poked into his basket tickling him gently on the nose.

"We'll be back before you know it," he was assured and then they were off. He was left to the mercy of the young girl, who tied a ticket to his basket labelled 'Willi Whizkas cage number 9'.

Once his basket was opened, he considered making a dash for it, but instead refused to come out with as much determination as he had refused to go in!

"Come on now Willi, we've got everything you need," said the girl, "there's a litter tray, a nice bowl of cool water and I'll just go and get you some cat treats," with that Willi Whizkas was ejected from his cat basket and placed in cage 9. He looked around and then crouched in the corner. It was comfortable enough all right, in fact there was more room than in some of his favourite places around his house and garden. It was some minutes before he realised that there was an upstairs to his cage linked by a wooden ladder. He needed no further invitation to explore, and trooped up the ladder to find some nice soft blankets. "That'll do nicely to curl up on for a kip," he thought to himself but it was much too early for that. He found a hole in the cage by the side of the blankets, and poked his head through to discover another ladder leading outside into a wire-covered enclosure. On venturing outside for a look round he was greeted by a low growl from the cage on his left. He snapped his head round to see a small Persian cat glaring fiercely as if to say "Who are you and what are you doing here?" Willi Whizkas opened his mouth, curled his tongue and hissed back as loud as he could, to let everyone know who was the boss.

He failed to assert his authority, but succeeded in attracting attention; all the other cats were looking at him and he felt quite embarrassed.

Before the hiss had subsided the Persian had flung itself at the wire, returning Willi's hiss with an even harder stare. Willi Whizkas was startled, but a reassuring voice from the cage to his right suggested the he pay no attention to the Persian, his humans had called him Blossom when he was a kitten because he was so cute before 'the operation' (he knew precisely what that meant). Willi nodded, thinking that if he had been called Blossom then he too, would feel pretty miffed. The reassurance had come from Corporal Conkers, a dignified, striped old tabby cat.

"He's always the same, this is the third year running we have been in this cattery at the same time. He'll calm down in a day or so," but Willi Whizkas was far from convinced when he looked at the snarling bundle of fur!

The sound of cat treats being poured into a dish bought Willi Whizkas to his senses, and he shot up the ladder for lunch. He had been given a good helping and didn't think he could finish them all, but he had a jolly good try just in case they took away any that he left. Like all cats with a full tummy, he loved to have a good lick round his paws, face and bottom followed by an hour or two's sleep. If he was lucky in his dreams, he would catch the mouse that lived under the shed.

2 Intruder in the Camp

It was cat and mouse once again as Willi Whizkas dreamt his way into the evening. His eyes, although closed, still blinked; his whiskers twitched and his paws clenched as if diving in for the kill. He was back at home chasing the mouse round and round the garden, but never quite managing to close in for the kill. The mouse was always a squeak in front, and in Willi's dreams, just as in real life, the mouse would dart under the shed.

The days passed slowly, he grew more and more lazy with no playmates like his best friend Ginger Tompkins, a grey and white tomcat, and the mouse under the shed. He was totally bored. Then, when he was least expecting it, his cat basket was brought to cage number 9, he needed no prompting to jump in, being fairly certain that this was not to be a trip to the vets. He heard the familiar voices of his humans, who looked a little different somehow. Their skin was all red and peeling! Back home in his kitchen, creeping out of his basket, he couldn't decide whether to purr with love and gratitude for being home again, or to act all sniffy to teach his humans a lesson. Some things just couldn't wait, however, so he bounded into the garden then backed up to his favourite bush, flourished his tail, all four paws on a penny and was about to mark his territory with a jolly good spray when he realised things were not as they should be. He turned round and sniffed the leaves which should carry only his own scent, but not today. There was an intruder in the camp! He took this as a most serious threat indeed, as every cat likes to have his own territories. He sat down, and while considering the seriousness of the situation, spotted a pair of pale yellow eyes peeping at him from behind a lavender bush. Willi Whizkas arched his back, the hairs stood up all along his spine and he let out a small hiss followed by a deep growl.

The pale yellow eyes narrowed then froze into a fixed stare. Willi's threat had not been taken seriously. He moved sideways like a crab, but the intruder was unmoved. Willi Whizkas let out a series of short yowls only to be met by a long yawn. Then the intruder leapt out, and Willi Whizkas embarrassed himself by rolling on his back submissively. His indignity soon faded, however, and his whiskers arranged themselves into a smirk as he saw what stood before him was the most comical thing he had ever seen. It was a cat all right, with a large brown tabbyish head, long fur, a flat little nose and droopy whiskers. There was fur on his paws and he had a fabulous tail, but as for the rest of him Willi Whizkas still had difficulty coming to terms with what he saw. Where there should have been fur was pink veiny skin. Suppressing a laugh, Willi Whizkas stood up.

"Who and what are you? And what happened to your fur?"

The newcomer looked down sadly and began to tell his tale.

"I've just been adopted by the family at the bottom of this garden."

"Oh I know them," smiled Willi Whizkas, "their Persian cat, Piggles, died last year, the female human was heartbroken. Don't tell me you're a Persian looking like that?" He asked incredulously.

"Fraid so, but all my fur had to be shaved off because I was neglected at my last home, my fur all went into a matted lump, even worse I had a nasty dose of fleas. The more I tried to scratch them, the worse my fur became, nobody brushed or groomed me, so I was rescued and shaved. Do you think it will grow back?"

"I doubt it," smirked Willi Whizkas.

He looked closely at the new cat and noted that he had a crooked jaw. The stranger explained that he had been hit by a car at his last home and his humans believed that vets were too expensive, so his jaw had set crooked.

"I would have give anything to have been taken to a vet and properly looked after," sighed the strange looking stranger. Willi Whizkas felt guilty when he recalled how naughty he had been each time he had been taken to the vet, although at least he'd never managed to sink his fangs into the vet yet. The new cat went on to say that as well as a new home he had been given a new name. Previously he was known as Furballs, but now he was called Tushtots. At this Willi Whizkas exploded with laughter, but Tushtots, ignoring him went on to say that now he had a new home where he was loved, and got to sleep on the bed with his new humans so he didn't care what he was called. Willi Whizkas was green with envy as the nearest he got was inside the kitchen, he'd even been banned from the sofa since he had sicked up fur balls one night and got thrown out into the rain. He gave the newcomer another look, and the more he looked, the more he laughed. Tushtots stood up and Willi Whizkas noticed that he had a large baggy flap of skin hanging down from under his tummy, so Willi Whizkas laughed even more and remarked that it looked like a 'bag of udders', Tushtots had to laugh too.

"It's where my stomach used to be until I was neglected and not fed properly, my ribs stick out too."

"Oh dear," said Willi Whizkas with a serious tone, "Lets hope you fill out again soon. If there's one thing a cat likes it's a fat tummy to be tickled." Willi Whizkas decided that he liked Tushtots and thought he needed a bit of looking after.

"Well as long as you're on my patch," he said gazing round his garden as if to point out the extent of his boundary, "we'd better give you the guided tour."

The first place he took him to was the garden shed.

"This is my favourite place, well one of them, I've got lots really. If you're very quiet and keep very still, there's a little grey mouse that comes out from underneath looking for food in the garden. I try to catch him regularly, I'm sure I even got a paw to his tail once. It's great sport trying to catch him."

"Sounds great," enthused Tushtots, "perhaps we can set an ambush, you drive him towards me then I'll catch him for you."

"Not so fast," interrupted Willi Whizkas, "that mouse has got my name on it, if anybody's going to catch him, it's going to be me."

With that he pointed a sharpened claw at Tushtots to emphasise the point. They ambled on to the fishpond.

"You're not likely to catch much here," said Willi Whizkas, "but it's great fun staring at the water waiting for the fish to swim by. It's tempting to dive in after one, but they are so, so quick all you would end up with would be a good soaking."

"What about frogs?" Tushtots enquired, "Do you get frogs in the spring?"

"Yes we do," replied Willi Whizkas thoughtfully, "I'd forgotten all about them," as a gleam came into his eyes. "Now they are good fun, especially when they're away from the water; you can chase them around the lawn and the flower beds, but they're very slimy and difficult to chew so I just play with them, they always get back to the pond eventually." The cats moved on to another of Willi's favourite places, a rough patch of cat mint which looked rather the worse for wear.

"This is heaven," drooled Willi Whizkas "There's nothing I like better than sniffing cat mint and rolling over on it. I don't quite know what comes over me but I go all funny and roll round miaowing for ages until I come to my senses again. Sometimes my humans try and tickle my tummy when I'm doing rolling around, I forget what I'm doing and give them a nasty bite. I don't mean to, it's just the cat mint biting!" Tushtots took a sniff of cat mint, it only took a few seconds for his eyes to glaze over.

"Aaaah I can feel myself going," Tushtots purred.

"We'll I'm afraid you'll have to get your own cat mint bush," Willi Whizkas retorted rather selfishly. The bird-table was last stop on the tour of Willi's favourite spots.

"My humans put scraps on here, nothing that we would eat, but the birds like it, mostly old bread and nuts in winter. It's great fun jumping up to try to catch them, but it's a bit too high and the birds always see me coming then fly away. You do get a good view of them from the kitchen window, though, on cold damp days I just look through the window watching them come and go imaging which one I'd like to catch most!"

"That's easy," laughed Tushtots, "a plump sparrow is by far the juiciest, although I have heard that starlings are an acquired taste."

"That's about it," declared Willi Whizkas, "these are some of my favourite spots in my garden, but I do go through a hole into your garden. Piggles the old Persian cat who lived there previously didn't mind, besides I think you and I are going to be pals, as long as you don't chase my mouse, which reminds me, it must be getting towards teatime now, my tummy always tells me when it's feeding time. Boring old cat meat from a tin I expect, it always seem to be the same sort from a green tin. Just because you like it the first time they give it to you they think that they have to give you the same old stuff for life, sometimes I don't bother to eat it even though I'm starving in the hope that they'll get the hint, but it hasn't worked yet."

"You poor thing," sympathised Tushtots, "I don't get food out of a tin unless its salmon or tuna. I mainly get hand fed with scraps of chicken or ham by my new humans and there's always a bowl of cat treats for me to help myself to. You must come over sometime Willi, my catflap is always open." At that they rubbed noses and parted, but as Tushtots walked away Willi Whizkas still couldn't help smirking at the bag of udders swinging from side to side under his tummy.

3 Ginger Tompkins

His humans had gone to work and as usual on summer days Willi Whizkas had been tempted outside with the lure of fresh cat meat then the door was firmly closed and locked behind him.

"So that's me out for the day," he muttered to himself. After eating his breakfast he climbed on the fence then up onto the garage, where he had a good wash of his paws and whiskers, yawned, then stretched right down to the tip of his tail before lying down in the morning sunshine. It's a well known fact that a lazy cat can sleep up to 18 hours a day, so it's never too early to snooze! Some time later he was rudely awoken when the bin wagon rattled its way up the street to take away the rubbish. He hated the bin wagon, he'd had one or two close shaves with it when he used to pop across the road to see old Gordon. If Gordon wasn't around he would creep through his cat-flap and polish off his breakfast for him. Willi Whizkas peeped over the garage roof and waited for the clattering wagon to go round the corner and out of sight.

"I'm glad that's gone," he yawned, "now I can decide what to do for the rest of the morning before my afternoon nap."

It didn't take him long to make up his mind. It had been ages since he had been to see his oldest pal, Ginger Tompkins, who lived a few gardens away. The journey was often eventful, so he had to be especially alert, but it was always worth it to see his pal. He sprang down from the garage, across the lawn then through the hole in the hedge as a blackbird cluck, cluck clucked at him from the safety of a cherry tree.

"Could be a nest there somewhere," he thought, licking his lips. It was usually worth a climbing up to check it out, but not today. He crossed Tushtot's garden, but there was no sign of him.

"No doubt being spoilt, lying on the bed being fed scraps," he pondered enviously. But Willi Whizkas thought he would rather have revolting tinned food all his life than look as ridiculous as that shaved Persian cat. He jumped up and over the wood panel fence then into another garden. No cat or dog lived here, but he had to keep an eye open for the human, who was very keen on gardening. There was nothing Willi Whizkas liked better, in times of need, than to dig a hole or two in the soft dark soil amongst the vegetables, to which the human who lived there would respond by spraying him with a water pistol, or at the very least by banging on the window. Willi Whizkas couldn't see what the problem was, he always buried his 'treasure' when he had finished. He sniffed round and selected a nice quiet spot to do just that, but it's funny how the first hole he dug never seemed quite right he always had to dig another two or three. He was just about to do what cats do in holes in the ground when an old football crashed through the onions followed by an angry shout!

"Clear off you little devil go do it in your own garden!" Willi Whizkas smirked, showed him a clean pair of heels and dived under the fence, the quickest he was likely to move all day. Now he had to be careful. In the next garden, which was the last one before Ginger Tompkins' house, there was a nasty little Jack Russell, although he was only about the same size as Willi Whizkas he could run very quickly, had a very loud bark and very, very sharp teeth. Some days the dog was out and Willi Whizkas knew when to scarper. But on a good day the Jack Russell would be inside the house sitting on the other side of the patio windows. Now this really was fun for Willi Whizkas. Knowing that the dog couldn't get out, He would saunter up the garden path making sure that the dog could see him, as this was guaranteed to unleash a furious spate of growling, snapping, barking, teeth showing and jumping up and down at the window. If he had the time to spare he would just sit a couple of inches away from the window nonchalantly licking his paws, whilst watching the dog work itself into a mad frenzy, at which point, unable to contain his laughter, he would turn round, tail erect, and pad back up the garden feeling thoroughly satisfied. But things had gone horribly wrong one day when a human unexpectedly turned up and opened the patio window. The Jack Russell hurtled down the garden snapping at Willi's paws. He got so close that Willi Whizkas could feel hot breath on his pink bottom! Only a heroic leap onto the wall at the bottom of the garden saved his bacon. With his heart in his mouth he had turned to see the Jack Russell jumping up at the wall snapping and growling, so he dropped his bushy tail down just out of the dog's reach in order to tease him some more!

"Another one to me," he thought satisfyingly.

However, this particular day was fairly uneventful, as Willi Whizkas jumped down and went to explore Ginger's garden, knowing all his favourite spots. He looked behind the garage, he went up to the house and looked through the French window, but there was no sign of Ginger, so where was he? Just as he was about to give up and go back home, Ginger darted out from behind a large flower pot and jumped onto Willi's back. The pair of them rolled round and round play fighting, when they had had enough of this Ginger Tompkins panted.

"Hello old chap, long time no see."

"I've been away in a cattery, only just got back to find a new kit on the block, name of Tushtots."

"Tush what?"

"Tushtots." Willi Whizkas repeated.

Ginger Tompkins grinned from ear to ear "Sounds a bit of a girlie name to me old thing. Rather like Twinkle Toes or Tickle Tums."

"Yes, but Tushtots is a special case, he's had a very sad life."

"Do you know I thought there was a fresh scent on the breeze," replied Ginger Tompkins.

"Just wait till you see him," chuckled Willi Whizkas "his body had been shaved and his saggy starved tummy hangs down like a bag of udders and wobbles from side to side as he walks." At this both toms collapsed laughing.

"The cheeky so and so thought that my garden was up for grabs while I was in the cattery, but I soon put him right," Willi Whizkas chortled. "I think he will turn out to be a decent sort of a cat providing he keeps his paws off my mouse. You must come over and I'll introduce you."

"Yes I must do that, how about tomorrow?"

"What have you got planned for today?" Willi Whizkas enquired.

"Well, I thought given the time of year, we could take a stroll over to the allotments, to see if we can catch some of those white butterflies that flutter around the cabbages."

"Good-oh, can't wait," Willi Whizkas purred excitedly.

"First things first Willi, I have to go and finish off my breakfast - coming?"

The two cats squeezed through Ginger Tompkins' catflap and finished off the breakfast. After much paw-washing, whisker-wiping and bottom-polishing the cats were ready to set off. They had to dash across the road, down a gravel lane to the allotments, which were where old human males went to grow flowers and vegetables and sit in their tiny sheds drinking tea from a flask reading their newspapers whilst eating cheese sandwiches which had been wrapped in foil. The cats threaded their way through racks of runner beans, peas and funny oniony things until they came to a large patch of cabbages. They had a quick look round to make sure that they weren't being watched, then started stalking butterflies.

"Any sign of anything yet?" Willi Whizkas shouted to Ginger Tompkins.

"Not a sausage old fruit," called Ginger Tompkins, "perhaps it's not sunny enough or the cabbages aren't cabbagy enough or something."

The cats didn't have to wait long until a large white butterfly fluttered over the rhubarb patch then landed on a cabbage leaf. It sat there for a moment or two opening and closing its wings in the sunshine. The two cats approached from different directions, fixing their stares on the butterfly. They were getting very close, almost within pouncing range, but neither Willi Whizkas or Ginger Tompkins were quite aware where each other was exactly, it wasn't until they both sprang at the same time and their heads bumped in mid-air that they became painfully aware of the pitfalls of hunting in pairs. So with sore heads they sat on the warm soft earth, gave up butterflies as a bad idea, and decided to bask in the sun instead. There was always buzzing in the air at the allotments; flies, bees, wasps, always something worth whipping a paw out for and having a swipe at. The next thing they heard was a gentle voice beckoning "Puss, Puss, Puss." The humans had this misconception that all cats were called Puss. But it was often worth investigating, especially when someone was holding out a titbit. It was an old man with a red bicycle who liked cats, he would often share his cheese sandwich with them, which probably tasted better than butterflies anyway! The old man gave both of them a good stroke and tried to get them to roll over so that he could tickle their tummies. Willi Whizkas liked to be stroked, but Ginger Tompkins would grab the mans hand with his front paws and kick with his back paws when he had had too much tickling, which made the old man laugh. They lay on the ground for some time by the old man, but when the sky turned black and large drops of rain began splattering to the ground throwing up dust, Willi Whizkas and Ginger Tompkins agreed that it was time to head home. They threaded their way back through the maze of sheds, water butts and wheelbarrows, back up the gravel lane, then over the road to Ginger's house. In the kitchen they jumped onto the work surface and sat at opposite ends of the window looking into the garden watching the rain, which made Ginger Tompkins thirsty so he lapped at the drops of water falling from the taps. Ginger Tompkins always preferred to 'steal' water rather than drink what was given to him.

"Well, must be off Ginge," laughed Willi Whizkas as he bounded through the cat-flap before retracing his paw-prints.

4 Tigaz

Willi's eyes were glazed over in the sort of trance like daze that can only come from a thorough session of catnip sniffing and a good roll with all four paws in the air to finish off, which is how Ginger Tompkins found him on the afternoon of Tigaz arrival. Ginger's humans were looking after Tigaz whilst its owners went on holiday. He couldn't get much sense from Willi Whizkas for a few minutes until the effect of the catnip had worn off, but once he looked sane and sensible enough, Ginger Tompkins began to tell his tale.

"Willi, how long have we known each other? Since we were kittens? Well, what I am about to tell you is true. I've fallen in love with the most gorgeous Bengal cat in the world. Even the name Tigaz sets my heart aflutter," he sighed dreamily

"What are you dribbling on about, fallen in love with Tigaz, what are you? You're not turning into a puffy cat are you?" Willi Whizkas retorted.

"Certainly not! You don't understand, Tigaz is a girl cat."

"What!" Exclaimed Willi Whizkas, his eyes wide open. "A girl? But you've been to the vet haven't you? You've had 'The Operation' haven't you?"

"Yes," Ginger Tompkins sighed, "but I think it's beginning to wear off. You really must come round as see her for yourself, she's beautiful!"

"But are you sure she's really a girl? Have you checked?"

"Didn't need to old sausage," smirked Ginger Tompkins." As soon as she got out of the cage her tail was in the air and she was strutting round like she owned the place."

"Gosh! But what does she think of you?" Willi Whizkas enquired.

"Not too sure about that old boy, I went over for a quick sniff and she swotted the top of my head with a paw full of claws and hissed, but she could be playing hard to get!"

"Right. Let's go and check her out," shouted Willi Whizkas as they raced off. They ran through the hole in the fence across Tushtots' garden, keeping an eye out for the Jack Russell. He was inside his house by the patio windows, so the cats ran up to the startled dog and stared at him. The dog went berserk, so they fled hell-for-leather over the wall into Ginger Tompkins' garden, then strolled across the lawn to the cat flap.

"I'd better go in first," volunteered Ginger Tompkins, "just to make sure the coast is clear." He pushed against the cat flap with his nose but it wouldn't move!

"What's the matter?" Willi Whizkas enquired impatiently.

"It won't budge, I think it's been blocked to stop Tigaz getting out and running off."

"That's a nuisance," said Willi, "how can I see her unless we can get into the house?"

"There's always the old bathroom window routine," mused Ginger Tompkins, so they scrambled onto the fence and leapt onto the garage roof. It was only a short hop onto the bathroom windowsill from there, the bathroom window was open just enough for the cats to squeeze through. Ginger Tompkins clawed feverishly at the bathroom door to try and pull it open as the wind had blown it shut, but eventually they got through.

"Right Willi we're in, let's go and see if we can find her."

They had a good sniff round upstairs first, then went into each bedroom in turn, looked on the beds, under the beds then behind the curtains, but she wasn't anywhere to be found. The cats went downstairs and the search continued in the breakfast room, but there was still no sign.

"I think you're making this up," accused Willi Whizkas impatiently. "No sign of her anywhere."

"I bet she's curled up on the sofa, I'll bet you anything!"

The toms nosed their way expectantly into the lounge, and they weren't disappointed. They came face to face, or should that be nose to nose, with the most beautiful cat they had ever seen. She sat up, glared and hissed gently at them.

"There Willi, my old flower, what did I tell you?"

"Do you know something?" Willi Whizkas whispered when he could take his eyes of Tigaz, "I think my operation is wearing off too!" The cats shuffled closer but the hisses grew louder and louder until eventually she addressed them. "What do you two miserable common alley cats think you are doing, trying to talk to me?"

Common alley cats??!!" The cats exclaimed in unison and looked at each other.

"Yes," she hissed "I'm a pure bred show class pedigree don't you know, unlike you run of the mill moggies, I've got breeding," with that she lifted her delicate nose into the air and gave out a hummpf of disdain.

"Well, that's gratitude for you," growled Willi Whizkas to Ginger Tompkins "you take her in for a couple of weeks to save her going into the cattery and that's all the thanks you get."

"I know," replied Ginger Tompkins miserably, "but I just can't stop looking at her. My poor heart is pounding away, I shall never be the same again!" They then retreated to the kitchen to munch cat sweets and plan their next move.

"I think we should let her out and see if she runs away," muttered Willi Whizkas spitefully.

"You can't do that, what if she gets run over? We'll get the blame! But she is a bit snooty isn't she, Willi old thing?"

"Perhaps we should take Tushtots' advice on this as he's a pedigree too. We can't have Tigaz treating you like this in you own house, especially where affairs of the heart are concerned," joked Willi Whizkas. So with that off they went across the gardens, stopping to give the Jack Russell a very hard stare as they went to find Tushtots. They didn't have to look far, he was sitting in his garden looking up at the apple tree where a blackbird was pecking holes in an apple. They told him the story of Ginger Tompkin's guest, how badly she'd treated them and how she had the cheek to call them both 'common alley cats'.

"Well that's not very nice," Tushtots agreed, "Not the way for a pure-bred pedigree lady cat to behave at all."

"Perhaps she'll talk to you?" Willi Whizkas suggested, "after all you are a pure-bred pedigree Persian cat aren't you?"

"Yes I am, but I wouldn't know where to lay a paw on my birth certificate since I was rehomed," he joked.

"Well your fur's beginning to grow a bit, you look halfway decent, please have a word with her old chap," pleaded Ginger Tompkins. "Just explain to her that I have fallen in love with her." So they all raced round to Ginger Tompkins' house, in through the bathroom window then silently down the stairs to the lounge. But Tigaz was nowhere to be seen.

"Oh no," wailed Ginger Tompkins "she must have

got out through the bathroom window and got run over!" But just then Willi Whizkas spied her in the kitchen on top of the cupboard. She looked down with utter disgust at Willi Whizkas and Ginger Tompkins, but when Tushtots walked in behind them it was a different story!

"Hello," she mewed seductively "I can see that you are no alley cat, what is a pedigree doing with a pair of ragamuffins like these flea-ridden mogs?"

"How dare you be rude to my bestest pals in the whole world?" Tushtots spat angrily, but she just purred, whispering in his ear "wouldn't you rather have me as your best friend, handsome?" As she nuzzled round him. Tushtots was so angry, he took her to one side and told her in no uncertain terms that as she was a guest in Ginger Tompkins' house she should behave herself.

"You're right," she agreed after a moments thought, "I have been a bit rude and superior. If I have to be here for a couple of weeks I'd better not upset anyone." She went over to Ginger Tompkins and gave him a great big cat-kiss on his whiskers and hoped that they would be friends for the rest of her stay. Ginger Tompkins keeled over onto the carpet letting out a big sigh.

"Aaaah, she loves me, I've had a mog-snog," he purred jokely. Tushtots suggested that she joined their gang as an honorary member.

"But you have to pass a test first," he told her mischievously

"Oh dear, will it not be difficult for a cat of my high breeding?" She asked in a worried tone.

"No." The tomcats chorused, so Tigaz reluctantly agreed, they led her to the bathroom where she looked up at the open window and guessed what was coming next.

"I don't 'do' outside," she exclaimed snootily.

"You do when you're in our gang," with that the three toms squeezed through the window then down onto the garage roof. Tigaz wasn't at all sure as she looked down,

"It's too far!" She observed with a wobble in her voice.

"Come on jump, jumping is what cats do best," she was encouraged. Tigaz closed her eyes and leapt down onto the garage, from where she was soon coaxed down onto the ground. Tigaz had never felt grass under her pads before, it felt wonderful! 'Outside' smelt so good and the bird song was tantalising. They all sped off onto the wall of the Jack Russell's house and looked down.

"This is the test," explained Willi Whizkas, "there's a nasty Jack Russell dog who lives here." Tushtots went on to explain that the test was to run up to the patio window, stare very hard at the dog until he goes ballistic, then run back. Which is precisely what Tigaz did, but she was so good at it that the toms had to jump down and go and pull her away from the window, she was enjoying it so much!

"That was the most fun I've ever had," she laughed, "we must do it again sometime." With that Ginger Tompkins took her home, while Willi Whizkas and Tushtots headed for their own gardens.

"Do you know what?" Tushtots announced, "I think my operation is wearing off!!!

5 Tigaz Adventure

It was a damp morning when Willi Whizkas turned up at Ginger Tompkins' house, he jumped onto the wall to look for his pal. Ginger Tompkins was sitting in the kitchen window looking out at the birds when he spotted him, so he jumped down and started miaowing at the door. The cat flap was still locked to keep Tigaz in, so every time Ginger Tompkins wanted to go out or come in he had to miaow to inform his humans. Once out he skipped down the garden avoiding the damp patches on the lawn then scrambled onto the wall to join Willi Whizkas.

"That darn Tigaz is driving me mad old fruit," he grumbled "She keeps on and on about wanting to have another adventure."

"The problem is," moaned Willi Whizkas," how can we take her on another adventure? The bathroom window is closed, the catflap is locked, obviously we need to use cat-cunning."

"I know just the thing," announced Ginger Tompkins after a moment's thought. "You wait here." With that he dashed back to the kitchen door and miaowed to be let in.

"You didn't stay out long, did you Ginge? Don't know what's got into you since Tigaz has been here," laughed one of his humans. Ginger Tompkins went looking for Tigaz, he found her on top of the wardrobe stretched out on an old blanket.

"Come on down," he shouted up to her "Willi is here, if you want to go for an adventure this is the plan. You hide behind the curtains while I miaow at the patio door, then when the door's open make a run for it to the wall at the bottom of the garden. Willi is waiting for us."

After much scowling from the human insisting he couldn't possibly want to go out because he had only just come in, Ginger Tompkins achieved his first objective.

"Oh, for goodness sake, go out," his human snapped "and don't come back until teatime." Just at that moment the postman happened to knock at the front door, so both cats slipped out and raced down the garden without being seen. Three tails now dangled over the garden wall side-by-side while the trio decided what sort of adventure Tigaz should have that day. It was nearly the end of her stay at Ginger Tompkins' house, both toms were still besotted with her, as was Tushtots, whom they were seeking at this present moment. They ran across the Jack Russell's garden into the vegetable patch next door. The human was out gardening, so they had to keep their wits about them and detour behind the compost heap.

"Phew! That stinks a bit, I suppose you alley-cats are used to such smells?" Tigaz chuntered.

"There she goes again, Lady Snot." Willi Whizkas muttered under his breath.

Compost heaps hold their own fascination. There were always large beetles beetling about, huge worms in the pile, the odd bluebottle or two to swot, sometimes there were horrible wriggly maggots. However they had no time today, they wanted to find Tushtots. They marched up the garden where he lived, but he was nowhere to be seen, so they sat and watched and waited for a while until boredom set in and they decided they'd have an adventure without him. There was always Willi's mouse under the garden shed to have a sniff at, but Willi Whizkas was keeping that for himself. They thought about the allotment but agreed that it was too damp for butterflies to be out, besides running through wet cabbages wasn't a good idea. So it was the Jack Russell or nothing! Off they scampered retracing their paw prints. The gardening man was putting slug pellets down, this time he saw them!

"Oi!" He yelled, clapping his hands loudly and throwing a clod of earth at them.

"Behind his greenhouse!" Willi yowled, "he won't throw anything else at us there!"

Squeezing through the fence they hid in a rather overgrown part of the Jack Russell's garden where they could not be seen. They looked for the dog, but couldn't see him. He wasn't at the patio windows which was good news. The Jack Russell's human was out sweeping the patio, so they waited until he'd gone in.

"We're not having much luck today," commented Tigaz sniffily, "I thought you toms had adventures every day, strikes me you have just as boring a time outside as I do inside."

Be patient," answered Willi Whizkas firmly, just as the skies cleared, the sun came out. All three cats pointed their noses to the sun and warmed themselves for a while, cats love to sunbathe just as much as humans do, they were about to doze off when a loud bark from the Jack Russell brought them to their senses. He'd been out for a walk with his other human and had come in via the back gate, where she let him off his lead! The trio crouched low in the undergrowth as the Jack Russell trotted down the path, hoping he hadn't seen them.

"Just stay put," whispered Willi Whizkas to the others in a low voice, as the dog's human whistled to him from the kitchen door. "Come on Jacko."

"Well blow me," muttered Ginger Tompkins, "I thought dogs had a keen sense of smell!" Just at that moment the grass tickling Tigaz' nose made her sneeze loudly. Jacko turned smartly round, his ears pricked up, his eyes narrowed he let out a volley of barks and ran as fast as his stubby little legs would carry him towards the astonished adventurers.

"Run for it!" Ginger Tompkins commanded, he clambered the wall first, with Willi Whizkas only a whisker behind. But Tigaz, still bleary-eyed from the sneeze, was slow off the mark, Jacko caught her by the ankle, sinking his teeth to the bone. Tigaz let out a huge banshee wail as the other two cats looked on horrified. But Tigaz had more sense that the toms gave her credit for. She turned on her good leg then sank her teeth and claws into Jackos' ear, causing him to let out a painful yelp and release her. The dog ran off whimpering and yelping in pain as Tigaz hauled herself onto the wall.

"Well done that girl-cat!" Ginger Tompkins applauded, but he could see blood trickling down her leg.

"That looks very nasty," observed Willi Whizkas "I hate to say it, but it looks like a job for the vet." The toms escorted the limping Tigaz back to Ginger Tompkins' house, and wailed urgently at the door to be let in. A bad tempered human opened the door.

"I told you not to come back till teatime," but then he noticed Tigaz. "How on earth did you get out?" Asked the amazed human. "You were asleep on the wardrobe when I last saw you." Ginger Tompkins shot into the kitchen, Tigaz limped sorely after him.

The human picked Tigaz up and tipped her upside-down in his arms. It didn't take long to spot the painfully swollen paw and bloodstained fur. "Oh dear, how are we going to explain this to your owners? You were supposed to be kept in, just look at you, you poor thing, looks like a trip to the vets." Tigaz was bundled off in her smart travelling cage and for several hours Ginger Tompkins padded anxiously round the house. When Tigaz returned complete with paw wrapped in white bandages, Ginger Tompkins went over to investigate, but was shooed away by the human and told that she needed plenty of rest. She was placed on a comfy cushion in the middle of the sofa and given encouraging strokes by the human, who assured her that she would be up and about in no time. Ginger Tompkins never got the scolding he expected, instead he was told he deserved a medal for finding Tigaz and bringing her home, not that he could understand anything his humans said. Quite how she got the dog-bite the humans couldn't imagine.

When the house was quiet Ginger Tompkins had a chance to sidle up to Tigaz and ask how things had gone at the vets. He was told all about the X-ray, the nasty smelling gas to breathe and how when she woke up her foot was all bandaged. The vet said nothing was broken, but she had to have some stitches.

"But you'll never guess what? While I was waiting to see the vet who should come trotting out of the vets on his lead looking very sorry for himself but Jacko, with his ear shaved and full of big black stitches, yelping and crying. So I hissed at him and he backed away and hid cowering behind his human! I guess Jacko's human asked him what on earth he was doing, how could he be frightened of a harmless cat, but he just shook with fear! I must rest now, but when my stitches come out I shall be as good as new," yawned Tigaz. The next day turned out to be the last day for Tigaz at Ginger's house, her humans were knocking on the door to come and collect their 'baby'. Ginger's humans had to explain the situation of how their darling kitten had come to grief. Ginger Tompkins looked askance as the doting female human picked up Tigaz and kissed her between her ears.

"My poor precious baby, what's happened to you? Mummy's home now and everything will be all right."

"Yuk, fancy allowing a human to kiss you," thought Ginger Tompkins to himself, the nearest he got to affection these days was a quick stroke when his dinner was put down for him. He preferred to spend as much time as possible having adventures with his pal Willi Whizkas, although on cold winter evenings he did like a nice warm human lap to stretch out on.

6 Willi's Trifling Affair

It was all go in the kitchen when Willi Whizkas returned from an unsuccessful mouse-catching operation. There were no scraps on the floor for him, not even a bowl of water, his litter tray was outside, the contents smouldering gently in the sunshine.

"No time for you today, catkins, you'll have to see to yourself I'm afraid. Go catch yourself a nice plump sparrow, I've got a party to organise so off you pop I don't want you dropping hairs, fleas or anything else in my nice clean house."

He wasn't really sure what a 'party' was but it sounded like trouble, especially if it meant no breakfast for him. As for a nice plump sparrow, it had been three weeks since his last frantic effort which had resulted in an embarrassing fall from the garden shed as the birds had squeaked and snickered in the trees. He jumped onto the kitchen work surface to see if there was anything there worth a nibble, but he was promptly picked up and decanted into the garden.

With "Stop being a pest Willi, I told you I haven't got time for you," ringing in his ears he padded miserably into the garden where he sat and pondered dejectedly. Work carried on in the kitchen, plates and cutlery were being clattered about, the fridge was being opened and closed, bottles were clinking. "It sounds like food," thought Willi Whizkas to himself, but one thing was for sure, there was none coming his way. It was a bit nippy in the garden, so he slipped back into the house to sleep on the television, which was one of his favourite spots, especially when it had just been switched off so was nice and warm. From up there he could see exactly what was going on. His female human was carrying lots and lots of food through to the dining room. One huge bowl in particular caught his eye. It was a decent size, whatever was in it was enough to keep him going for a whole week. It was pink at the bottom, white at the top and Willi Whizkas thought he could catch a faint scent of lip-smacking fresh cream. Soon plates of sandwiches were being carried through, he recognised some of the odours immediately. Chicken, possibly tuna, certainly succulent salmon. Willi's tummy rumbled and grumbled ever more loudly. Just as he thought no more food could possibly fit in the dining room his female human let out an exasperated cry.

"Darn it," she cursed "I've forgotten the serviettes." She obviously hadn't noticed Willi Whizkas sprawled over the television set watching the proceedings because he would most definitely have been turfed out!.

The front door slammed closed and the female human click-clack-clicked down the drive, then drove off. Now Willi Whizkas being a fairly smart sort of a cat started to put two and two together. He was hungry and 'party' obviously meant lots of food. This was too good an opportunity to miss.

He wasn't in the habit of stealing food, because he was over fed anyway, but this was different! He yawned then slithered off the television, then padded lazily over to the dining room. The air was heavy with a multitude of delicious fragrances which screamed 'FOOD'. He jumped onto the sideboard first, from where he had an excellent view of the table. Now he could plan his best route of attack. He leapt up, but as he did so he bumped into a tall round object wrapped in brightly coloured paper, which toppled over and fell with a crash. "OOPS," he giggled, as what sounded like a bottle smashed on the floor. The sideboard was covered in lots of coloured cards which fluttered down onto the carpet as he crept past them, even though he barely touched them. He then decided to go for the table, with a couple of bounds he was in the middle of more food than he had ever seen at any one time! He didn't know which way to look first, he sniffed the chicken sandwiches, salivated on the salmon, then his teeth chattered in anticipation over the prawn vol-au-vents. Where was a cat to begin? "Time to dip my snout," he smirked to himself, and with that he dived at the salmon, which was probably the nicest thing he had ever been given, or should that be helped himself to? After a few deep bites into the soft pink flesh his attention turned to the chicken sandwiches, where his tongue carefully teased some of the tender slices out of the bread. The butter-smeared chicken was almost as tasty as the salmon. What could he try next? There were some cold sausages on sticks but he concluded that they weren't as nice as the other things, although had he found them on the lawn outside he would have scoffed them in a trice! Then he discovered the 'piece de resistance'!! The large bowl he had seen being carried through earlier was full to the brim with strawberry trifle, topped with cream, hundreds and thousands, and a scattering of cherries. There was something about the smell of fresh cream that made his eyes glaze over, it almost had the same effect as cat mint, before he knew what he'd done, he'd reared up on his back legs and plunged himself up to his neck in soft gooey heaven! His tongue lapped and lapped until he thought it could lap no more, they say that every dog has his day, well Willi Whizkas thought that also applied to cats because today was definitely his day! He was so full by now his tummy was full to bursting, it felt like his fur was stretching to the limit What he needed most of all now was to have a good snooze.

He thudded down heavily from the table, knocking over an open bottle of red wine in the process which glugged all over the white table cloth. He shook his head, the cream off his face and whiskers splattering all over the furniture, walls and carpet. He returned to the television to stretch out and have a nap, but he couldn't sleep, his bloated tummy still wanted more of the heavenly treats just a few feet away!

He waddled into the kitchen to see what other goodies had his name on, hoping for more cream. There was a smell of baking cake coming from the oven, but Willi's nose led him to the swing bin by the kitchen door, where something was making his nose twitch. He stretched up as far as he could and nosed the flap in front of him, which promptly swung back then hit him firmly on the nose. So he went around to the other side of the bin and tried again. He pushed the flap with his nose and sure enough it swung back again. He was beginning to get the message so he pushed it even harder, it swung back further, just enough for him to get his head and paws in before it swung back again. If he could just get a little bit further in he might be in with a chance of a lick of the cream pot whose aroma was enticing him to the bottom of the bin. His back paws scrabbled to get a grip, but the bin lid swung back hard and wedged him in the perfect position, upside down in the bin with his nose in an almost empty cream pot. Heaven! Just like all cats, he knew that the best, the very bestest bit of anything is the very last lick!

Just at the worst possible moment from Willi's point of view the front door opened, although he was too busy to notice. The kitchen door followed and the female human let out the loudest, shriek Willi had ever heard,

"Willi, you daft cat! What on earth are you doing, how the devil did you get stuck in the bin?" No matter how much he struggled he was firmly wedged in the bin, his back legs caught by the bin flap and his head stuck in the cream pot. It was a very undignified position for any cat to be in. He was hauled out unceremoniously by the tail, at which point the dreadful cream-covered mess that he was in was revealed.

"What have you been doing Willi you hopeless thing?" She laughed at him. "It's a fine mess you've got yourself into." She took him by the scruff of his neck to the sink and wiped him down with a flannel. At this point she caught a strong whiff of salmon, which was odd as there were no salmon scraps in the bin. Dropping Willi Whizkas, she raced into the dining room fearing the worst. The table was an utter shambles, the red wine soaked tablecloth was dripping onto the carpet, sausages were scattered across the table, there were holes in the salmon, and the chicken-less sandwiches were strewn everywhere. There was also a strong smell of after shave from the package which lay broken on the floor. The female human pressed her hands to the side of her face and she let out a scream

"WILLI!! You are the world's naughtiest cat You wait till I get my hands on you. It's taken me all day to do this and you've destroyed it all in twenty minutes. It's supposed to be for John's surprise party!"

Willi Whizkas was halfway down the garden before his paws touched the ground, his backside smarting. He hid under the bushes and heard food being scraped off plates. His male human arrived at this point unaware that a surprise party had been planned for him, but when he saw the carnage he burst out laughing.

"Never mind," he giggled, "throw it down the garden for the birds. I'll go and fetch a Chinese takeaway before the guests arrive." A bit of quick thinking now on Willi's part just might see the situation turning to his advantage, and that of Tushtots and Ginger Tompkins. He rounded them up as speedily as possible, soon the cats were tails up, noses down snuffling through the grass for the most tempting titbits they had ever had.

"How come there's such good scraps for the birds on your lawn?" Enquired Tushtots.

"It's a long story!" Willi Whizkas replied. Later, when he ventured inside the house again, his female human had gone to bed, the male was scraping the remains of the Chinese takeaway (one of Will's favourites), into his cat bowl.

"You are well and truly in the dog house," his male human told him "You don't deserve these." "Crikey," thought Willi Whizkas, "I'm fit to burst. Still, they'll taste just as good in the morning, cold and congealed." So he leapt onto the work surface, let out a satisfied burp, then fell asleep.

7 Tushtot'sCatflap

aving just woken up, still yawning, Willi Whizkas was sorely tempted to curl up and go back to sleep. His humans were busy watching tennis on television, so he took his chance and went upstairs. Willi Whizkas had been read the riot act recently by his humans; he could sleep on the sofa or TV if he really had to, but clawing the furniture was out, as was sleeping on the bed, due to his propensity for shedding fur and fleas. He could drink from the toilet, if he really had to be so disgusting, but if the bathroom door blew closed behind him he was not to claw the carpet up by scratching frantically, but wait patiently on the wash basket until he was let out. Not that anything the humans ever said to him made any sense, but cats know what they should and shouldn't do, so Willi Whizkas knew exactly where his boundaries were. However, seeing the sliding mirror doors of the wardrobe had been left to one side, he thought he might have a nose round just for the fun of it, "You never know, there may be a mouse in there," he thought hopefully. There wasn't, but what he discovered was the next best thing, his female human's favourite cashmere sweater, neatly folded, just begging to be sat on! He wearily climbed onto the shelf and began kneading the jumper with his paws, turning round as he went, whilst his sharp claws picked at the threads. He loved how cosy it felt and settled down for a good bottom wash, ear scratch and fur chew, spitting out a few tatty remnants onto the sweater before settling down to the serious business of sleeping.

Rain having abandoned play at the tennis the humans decided to go shopping, so the female human came into the bedroom to change her clothes. She didn't notice Willi Whizkas at first, but when she did, Oh boy was he in trouble. He was grabbed unceremoniously by the scruff of the neck and given a jolly good finger-wagging type talking to, followed by lots of screaming and yelling when she saw the mess the jumper was in.

"Why do you always have to be so naughty you bad cat? How many times do we have to tell you?" Yet again he found himself dumped in the garden with the door locked behind him. Ears flat to the head, he settled under the bushes out of harm's way. He was just beginning to recover from his scolding and becoming vaguely interested in the birds pecking away on the bird table when who should come through the hole in the fence but Tushtots. He was crouching very low, moving slowly one leg at a time, making a definite beeline for the garden shed. This wasn't Tushtots' normal route, usually he would come miaowing up the path to the kitchen door to attract attention.

"I know just what he's up to," Willi Whizkas deduced "He's after my mouse!" Tushtots had now reached the shed and was peeping underneath with a paw fully extended ready to grab, but in just two bounds Willi Whizkas was across the garden scratching and biting at Tushtots ears. The Persian cussed and spat as he wasn't sure who his attacker was, but on realising it was Willi Whizkas he sprang back, eyes as black as coals, he let out a hissing snarl.

"Oh, it's you Willi," said Tushtots breathlessly, "I was just looking for you."

" You were looking all right but not for me," snarled Willi Whizkas "I told you when you first came here, that mouse has my name on it, I'll thank you to leave it alone."

Tushtots decided to change the subject in the hope that Willi Whizkas would forget about his precious mouse.

"I've got a surprise to show you Willi, but we need to get Ginger Tompkins first." So off they went to seek out Ginger. They shot through the garden next door, then through the Jack Russell's garden, unnoticed by human or canine. Once they were in Ginger Tompkins' garden they didn't need to look too hard for him as he was on his way to look for them! The cats greeted each other with some serious sniffing after which Tushtots said "Come on boys, wait till you see what the humans have got me this time!"

After leading them through his garden, then up to the kitchen door Tushtots turned round and asked "Well, what do you think?" Willi Whizkas and Ginger Tompkins just looked at each other.

"What do we think about what?" They asked, puzzled. "This," said Tushtots pointing a claw. "A new cat-flap." Said Willi Whizkas, who had always yearned for just such a thing.

"You'll find that useful old bean," commented Ginger Tompkins, "I've always had one, wouldn't be without one." Willi Whizkas was green with envy, he was now the only tom on the block without a cat-flap, but he tried to look pleased for Tushtots all the same.

"Come on boys, give it a try! Lets christen the cat-flap, there's some choice cuts of chicken and ham lying inside, just waiting for us to scoff!"

This sounded too good to be true, the three of them dashed to the catflap, where an untidy pile of legs, tails and heads ensued as, of course, they all tried to scramble through at the same time.

Once the cats had sorted themselves out Willi and Ginger rapidly ascertained that there was no sign whatsoever of the promised feast. "Can't see any food,"

Willi Whizkas grumbled. "Nor can I," agreed Ginger Tompkins. "You have got some?" They both asked Tushtots. "Oh yes," he confirmed, deftly opening the fridge door with an agile left paw. Willi Whizkas and Ginger Tompkins were suitably impressed

"Where on earth did you learn that neat little trick?" asked Ginger Tompkins.

"When you've been neglected like I was you learn to fend for yourself, besides the humans here think this trick is quite enchanting, so they've given me my own shelf for my scraps," at which he proceeded to drag a plastic bag from the fridge onto the floor. Willi Whizkas and Ginger Tompkins whiskers twitched in anticipation. "Smells good to me," sighed Willi Whizkas, "Beats that stuff that comes out of a tin."

"O.K. follow me," commanded Tushtots as he picked up the bag in his mouth and led the way upstairs to the master bedroom where there was a huge king-size bed with a woolly blanket spread across the bottom.

"That's where I sleep," Tushtots pointed out, "when I'm not actually in the bed with my humans."

"You actually sleep with humans?" asked Ginger Tompkins incredulously. "Oh yes, it's nice and cosy on cold nights and my humans really appreciate a good purr!"

"Just wait till you've given them fleas," commented Willi Whizkas "You'll be turfed out as quick as anything!"

"No chance" replied Tushtots "I get regular treatment now." The cats dragged the bag onto the bed then tore into it, picking the largest pieces their mouths could manage and gnawing away at cool tender chunks of chicken and ham. Willi Whizkas and Ginger Tompkins both agreed that the catering at Tushtots' house was first class, but Willi Whizkas couldn't help observing that it wasn't as good as the cream trifle he had so recently stolen, the three cats chortled at the memory of that incident. Now cats are by nature, very predictable, so a lot of washing and pampering followed, but before the predictable catnap could commence Willi Whizkas looked at the greasy mess on the duvet.

"I think you'll be in trouble Tushtots, just look at the mess we've made. If this were me I'd be out on my ear."

"Me too!" Ginger Tompkins agreed.

"Well I don't think I have anything to worry about, I've never been told off about anything since I came to this house," Tushtots told them. The cats wriggled their way under the duvet, put their heads on the pillows and one by one they drifted off to sleep. Had anybody been there to listen, the sound of contented feline snoring would have been heard throughout the house. Eventually human footsteps climbing the stairs brought the cats back from the land of nod. Willi Whizkas held his breath in fear, surely they were going to be for it? Not a bit of it, for when Tushtots' human came into the bedroom and saw the three toms rubbing sleep out of their eyes with their paws he just smiled kindly.

"Goodness, what have we here, are these your little pals, Tushtots?"

"You see", whispered Tushtots to Willi Whizkas, "Give them what they want and they'll adore you, you can get away with murder, try it sometime, Willi. The other thing my humans love is when I roll over and let them tickle my tummy." At that moment the male human called the female to come and look at what he'd found.

"Aaaah, aren't they just adorable," she gushed, "the 'Three Mogateers'!!"

Both humans tickled all three cats until they couldn't purr any louder.

"No claws remember boys," Tushtots whispered as he purred. The humans then went back downstairs, only to return with a big bag of fresh prawns which they fed each cat in turn. The cats ate, purred and ate until they could eat and purr no more, then the duvet was tucked back over them and they were left to it.

"This is heaven, I wish I could live here old fruit!" Ginger Tompkins sighed.

"You're both welcome to drop by now that I have my new catflap, but remember I'm dominant tom here, only I get to open the fridge, and no spraying!!!"

As it was getting dark Tushtots' humans woke the cats from their slumber and suggested it was probably time they were getting off home, besides which the duvet cover needed changing! So Willi Whizkas and Ginger Tompkins trotted down the stairs, thanked Tushtots for a wonderful afternoon, not to mention the fabulous food, and begged could they do it again sometime soon, please, please, please!! Willi Whizkas and Ginger Tompkins certainly envied Tushtots his well -trained humans.

"But he was really badly neglected before he came here," Ginger Tompkins pointed out. "I would have hated being shaved all over, it's taking ages to grow back, he's only just starting to look normal. Anyway you have a good home old thing, if you weren't such a naughty cat, you'd probably get your own cat flap." Willi Whizkas tried to imagine sleeping with his humans, but thought the male was just that little bit too whiffy!

"You don't suppose the Jack Russell could get through a catflap?" Willi Whizkas asked.

"I wouldn't rule it out," replied Ginger Tompkins, "but I expect he's too stupid to work out how to use one!"

As the moon rose over the garden the two toms went their separate ways, Willi Whizkas padded up to his kitchen door letting out a ghostly yowl which would have to suffice until his humans bought him a catflap.

8 Stinker of the Yard

Willi's luck finally changed for the better. The lavender bush next to the lawn had grown into an ideal hide for him to crouch and watch the birds on the lawn. His humans were always throwing scraps onto the bird table, but for some reason that day they'd just thrown them onto the grass, which was no bad thing for Willi Whizkas as he eyed the sparrows and starlings with interest. Several opportunities came and went but just as he'd coiled up ready to pounce something would always disturb the birds and they would fly away. Blackbirds were good at giving the game away with their persistent cluck cluck clucking, warning other birds who would then take to the air. However this time everything was just right. There was a small group of sparrows who were so busy pecking away at the stale apple pie, they never saw him coming. This time he didn't miss, no sooner had he sprang than a warm fluffy sparrow was in his grasp. He was pretty sure that he hadn't bitten the sparrow, so he reasoned that it must have been sheer fright that had killed him. Whatever the reasons, a dead sparrow was a dead sparrow. He picked up the bird and trotted proudly towards the kitchen door.

Some cats love to show their humans how clever they are and take their trophies home to show them, Willi Whizkas was no exception, depositing the sparrow by the kitchen door. After looking at it then licking it a few times, he miaowed at the door to attract the humans attention, wanting someone to come and admire his handiwork. But his female human was far from pleased.

"You naughty cat," she shouted, "how could you, Willi, all the food we give you and you still have to catch birds!" With that she picked up the broom then chased him down the garden. So, minus one sparrow, Willi Whizkas ran off through the hole in the hedge into Tushtots' garden and safety. When he slunk back home an hour or so later there was no sign of the sparrow. He looked around for it but it had well and truly gone, his humans must have eaten it!

"Or maybe it wasn't really dead and flew away," he pondered.

That evening he was picked up by his male human and placed on the work surface, just as the female human came in holding a small brown paper bag.

"Now this is for you Willi," she said, opening the bag taking out a bright red collar with a large jingling bell and a name tag on which Willi's name and telephone number were engraved. The bell was to warn birds and mice of his approach.

"This should stop the little blighter catching birds," laughed the male human as the collar was snapped around Willi's neck. He had never had a collar before, although he had seen other cats wearing them. He shook his head and was almost deafened by the bell.

"Well, that's torn it," he thought. "Everything will know when I'm out and about." The mouse, the birds and most worryingly the snappy Jack Russell would be able to hear him coming from miles away. He sloped out of the house feeling thoroughly miserable, having lost a sparrow and gained a collar. It hadn't been a good day.

He had a restless evening, every time he turned over to get more comfortable the bell would jingle, which darkened his mood even more. He didn't dare show it to his pals Tushtots and Ginger Tompkins; Tushtots had a collar, but that just had his name on it, not a great big sissy bell. So he decided that he would spend the next few days in his own garden and sulk.

His absence had not gone unnoticed by Ginger Tompkins who decided to seek him out. He met up with Tushtots who said he hadn't seen Willi either so the pair of them set off to look for him. After sniffing around all Willi's favourite places in the garden they found him on the roof of the garage. Willi Whizkas looked slightly surprised to see them looking up at him, as he turned his head his bell jingled. Ginger Tompkins and Tushtots looked at each other then back to Willi Whizkas, or should that be Willi's collar and bell. Then grins started to develop on their faces until they couldn't contain themselves any longer and they burst out laughing. Willi Whizkas had known this would happen and he gave the pair of them a withering stare.

"Very nice," chortled Ginger Tompkins.

"It's what every fashionable feline is wearing this year, I'm sure," sniggered Tushtots.

"It's not through choice." Snapped Willi Whizkas

"Is it must be your birthday or something old fruit?" Ginger Tompkins enquired.

"I should be so lucky," moaned Willi Whizkas miserably, "this is more punishment than present!"

"Have you been a naughty cat again?" Tushtots teased.

"I'm afraid so," Willi Whizkas admitted with embarrassment, "I caught a nice plump sparrow a few days ago and I thought my humans would love to see it; a mark of my affection as I saw it and this is my reward."

"That's a bit of bad luck old chap," laughed Ginger Tompkins, "don't fancy your chances of catching anything now!!"

"I don't need to catch my dinner since I've been rehomed," commented Tushtots "I get all the fish and chicken I want!"

"All right, all right, don't rub it in," growled Willi Whizkas wearily. His diet was still the usual bland cat food from a green tin. As the days passed, he actually got used to his collar, on some occasions found it quite useful. Tushtots would hear him coming and meet him, Ginger Tompkins would hear him when he went through Ginger's catflap to say 'Hello', but most interestingly, the Jack Russell would come running down the garden barking at the merest jingle so Willi Whizkas always knew when it was safe to cross his garden. All was well with Willi's new collar until the Jack Russell caught him by surprise. Instead of running down the garden yapping, the dog was lying in wait behind a water butt, Willi Whizkas walked straight into the trap. The Jack Russell jumped out and Willi Whizkas froze for a second, so the Jack Russell was almost upon him before he moved. Willi Whizkas tried to escape through the nearest hedge, but his collar snagged! He snapped his head back in panic and tried again, just squeezing through to safety as the Jack Russell let out a stream of furious barking. It wasn't until the dust had settled and Willi Whizkas was back in his own garden that he noticed that his bell had stopped ringing. He sat down, scratching his neck to see what had happened. Not only was the bell missing, so too was the collar. His heart sank a little, he wondered what on earth could have happened to it, he'd better stay out this evening otherwise the humans might just notice it had gone. Tushtots sauntered into Willi's garden.

"Lost your collar, have you? I bet you're well rid of it."

"I was growing to like it, actually, it had its uses. Will you help me look for it Tushtots?"

"We'll call in Stinker of the Yard. He lives at the

police station down the road, he just might help with our enquiries. Don't get too near him, though, he's called Stinker because he eats the policemen's salami sandwiches and it gives him pongy breath . . . and a bit of a pongy bottom!"

So they sought out the famous Stinker of the Yard.

"Right, lets have the facts then lads," demanded Stinker. "When did you last see your collar?" Willi Whizkas told him the story about the run-in with the Jack Russell right up until the moment when he realised that his collar was missing.

"With all my years of police training . . . " began Stinker,

"Police training," muttered Tushtots "he's only that station mouser, a failed one at that!"

"I think we should retrace Willi's steps, reconstruct the events and examine all the evidence."

So they returned to the 'crime scene'.

"This carcass on the lawn," said Stinker officiously," It looks like homicide to me, do you know anything about this Sir?"

Willi Whizkas explained wearily that it was an old roast chicken carcass his humans had put out for the birds. They cautiously entered the Jack Russell's garden, although as it happened they were quite safe, the dog having been taken for a walk.

"Now, exactly where were you when the alleged ambush took place Sir?" Stinker enquired.

"Just here Stinker," said Willi Whizkas pointing a claw to the exact spot

"Now in your own words, what happened next?"

Willi Whizkas told his tale about the Jack Russell leaping out from behind the water butt snapping and snarling.

"Is this the hedge where you tried to make good your escape Sir?"

"Yes, absolutely, Stinker, in fact there's some of my fur snagged on the twigs."

Stinker looked at the sample of the fur and proclaimed "Exhibit 'A', I should send it off to the Pussology Lab for tests - Just my little joke, sir," but no matter how hard they looked there was no sign of Willi's red collar.

"I think this requires a fingertip, or should that be paw-tip search of the garden." Stinker instructed. The cats were ordered to spread out in an orderly manner and examine every inch of the area. After a few minutes Stinker halted the proceedings

"Hello, hello, hello, what have we here then?" He was standing by a mound of freshly dug earth and began to sniff it.

"I don't think you want to look there," smirked Tushtots with an embarrassed look on his face.

"Why ever not?"

"That was a fresh hole I dug this morning, I know exactly what's buried down there!!"

"Are you absolutely certain Sir?" Stinker asked, "have you any witnesses?"

"I hope not," Tushtots replied, "but I think that's one piece of evidence which is distinctly inadmissible!

"Aaaah, what have we got here?" Willi Whizkas exclaimed. Stinker stood to attention, keen to supervise matters. Pawful by pawful earth was removed only to reveal one of the Jack Russell's old chewed bones.

"Not having much luck are we Sirs?" Stinker commented. "Are you sure you're not wasting police time with this matter?"

"Don't be silly," retorted Tushtots, slightly annoyed at the allegation. "If he said he lost his collar here, then he lost his collar here." They decided to retire to the roof of the Jack Russell's coal shed to have a quick catnap before reviewing the evidence. They hadn't been there long when the patio door opened, out trotted the Jack Russell. Three pairs of eyes peeped over the edge of the coal shed amazed at what they saw, and indeed heard! The Jack Russell, holding Willi's collar proudly between his teeth, skipped down to the bottom of the garden, dug a hole into which he dropped the collar, then proceeded to bury it!!

"The villain is caught red-handed wouldn't you say Sirs?" Stinker whispered as the Jack Russell turned round and trotted back inside. The cats slid down off the back of the coal shed and retrieved the evidence.

"Is this definitely yours?"

"It most certainly is." Willi Whizkas responded

"Another crime solved by Stinker of the yard! Just one more thing sir, do you wish to confront the criminal with the evidence?"

"Oh, I think so," confirmed Willi Whizkas, the three of them marched up to the patio window where Willi Whizkas, collar in mouth, shook his head violently to jingle the bell. The Jack Russell threw himself at the window, jumping up and down, tearing at the curtains, and barking so furiously he attracted the attention of his human, who quickly rolled up a newspaper then gave him a good sound thwack on the bottom for being so noisy! Unfortunately he then spotted the cats watching with glee outside and banged on the window at them. The cats tore off to Tushtots' garden with all due haste where Willi Whizkas and Tushtots thanked Stinker for his help.

"All in the line of duty Sirs," he replied modestly, "now I really must be getting back to the station for my salami." As he passed Willi Whizkas and Tushtots they noticed a certain odour emanating from him. "No wonder you stood upwind of him," said Willi Whizkas, holding a paw to his nose,

"Now I know why they call him Stinker of the Yard!"

9 Gordon's Accident

It is not unknown for humans to tell cats their secrets, one day such an occasion arose when Willi Whizkas was dozing in the spare bedroom. His female human found him lying there and started to give him a good stroke, first on his head, then behind his ears, then along his back. Willi Whizkas was one of those cats who liked to have his back stroked, he would instantly stand up and put his tail into the air as far as it would go, but his absolute favourite was if his human scratched his back just where his tail joined on, which would produce a loud purr and a silly look in his eyes.

"You like that, don't you Wills?"

He replied with a soft miaow. It was then that she began to tell him all about an old tabby cat called Groucho she had when she was a little girl, and how she would try and smuggle him upstairs, hoping that he would snuggle down with her in bed, but somehow her mum would always find out and take Groucho back to the kitchen.

"It's a pity you aren't more affectionate and less naughty Willi," she sighed. Which, had Willi understood a single word she'd said, would surely have given him 'paws' for thought.

After his human left Willi Whizkas spotted Snapper the poodle, a dog famed in the cat world for his appalling attitude towards all things feline, taking himself for a walk on his own, which was bad news for any cat who happened to be out and about at the time. Unfortunately Gordon, a white cat with tabby markings, had just squeezed under his gate and was sitting on the drive washing his paws. Gordon was totally unaware that Snapper was about, it was only when Snapper crashed through the flowers on the front lawn that Gordon took to his heels and fled. Willi Whizkas would normally have enjoyed such a chase from a safe distance, he was just beginning to think how lucky he was to have such a grandstand view when events took a turn for the worse. The fleeing Gordon ran straight into the path of a postman peddling his bike up the road. What followed was a confusion of spinning wheels, a cursing postman, letters flying down the road, and Gordon lying in the road motionless. Postie wasn't sure what had happened at first, but when he saw Gordon he started to panic.

"I've killed him, I've killed him, Oh poor puss!"

Willi's human had also seen what had happened, and dashed out to see if she could do anything. Willi Whizkas just stared in horror at the carnage below. By now a small group of people had gathered, the dazed postman was tending a grazed elbow, the milkman was helping by chasing down the road trying to catch the letters. Gordon's human came out of the house crying, with a blanket. They wrapped Gordon's lifeless body up then took him into his house. Willi Whizkas muttered to himself,

"Poor Gordon's dead, I'm so sorry for stealing his cat meat."

A wave of sadness and remorse passed through him, but an hour or two later Willi felt able to cross the road to investigate the scene of the accident. There wasn't really much to see except a few tufts of Gordon's fur. "He won't be needing his food now," thought Willi Whizkas cheerfully, "It would be a shame to see it go to waste." With that he crept through Gordon's catflap, but there was no food there, his bowl of water was gone, even the box where Gordon slept was nowhere to be seen. It didn't look like they expected him back, perhaps Gordon had lost all nine of his lives.

Willi Whizkas was alone in the house, so he thought he would explore a little. A door was open at the far end of the kitchen so he poked his head, a couple of whiskers and an eye round it, only to be confronted by a truly awesome sight! A bird! In a cage! Willi Whizkas had never seen a bird in a cage before.

"What a lucky so-and-so that Gordon was to have such a plump specimen especially caught for him," he thought to himself as he moved in to get a better look. The magnificent bird had a big beak, long tail feathers and beady eyes which seemed to follow Willi Whizkas around. Willi Whizkas had just jumped onto the windowsill to get an even better look when a rasping voice came from somewhere,

"Love you Gordon, Love you Gordon who's a cute cat?" Willi Whizkas fled back into the kitchen in terror half expecting to see Gordon, but there was no-one there of course, no Gordon, no humans, nobody, just Willi Whizkas and the bird. He went cautiously back into the room for a second look, and heard in the same voice,

"Put the kettle on, put the kettle on, more tea vicar SQUAWK SQUAWK!!" It was only then that the penny dropped. It was the bird that was talking!

Willi Whizkas was amazed and disgusted, the bird had broken all animal laws. The odd miaow was O.K., but to actually talk to humans in their own language was forbidden! Willi Whizkas started to plan getting into the cage, the bird would make a tasty snack, and it would stop him talking!

"Where's Gordon? Where's Gordon?" The parrot shrieked at Willi Whizkas, who, realising the cage was just out of reach, decided to seek out Tushtots and Ginger Tompkins and tell them what he had found, along with the sad tale of Gordon's demise. Tushtots and Ginger Tompkins were shocked to hear about Gordon, but at the same time they couldn't wait to see Gordon's fabulous bird and hear it speak, which they still had their doubts about, a bird that could talk didn't seem possible.

Willi Whizkas led the disbelieving duo over the road, up the drive, under the garden gate and through Gordon's catflap. There was still no food on the floor, so they proceeded to the room in question.

"There, what did I tell you," said Willi Whizkas smugly, as six eyes trained themselves on the bird.

"Isn't it big?" Ginger Tompkins gasped, "look at the size of that beak, I wouldn't fancy being nipped by that!" Willi Whizkas told them that they would get a better view from the windowsill, so they all jumped up.

"I can't actually hear it saying anything," Tushtots pointed out,

"No, come to think of it nor can I old thing," added Ginger Tompkins.

"Well it spoke plain enough yesterday," confirmed Willi Whizkas. Then all three of them froze in surprise as the bird let out a piercing whistle, a couple of squawks and then "Gordon's home! Gordon's home!" After which a weak little voice from the other side of the room said "Yes, Gordon is home, what are you three doing here?" It was Gordon. Willi Whizkas yowled in disbelief, and jumped down to where Gordon lay on a soft blanket in the middle of the sofa. The other two cats joined Willi Whizkas, they all looked up at a hardly recognisable Gordon, with one back leg wrapped in a white bandage, his jaw wired together and a huge lampshade-type affair round his neck.

"Gordon? Gordon we thought you were dead!"

"'Fraid not," Gordon stated the obvious. "Although it was touch and go for a while. I'm not really sure what happened."

"I saw it all," said Willi Whizkas, " Snapper the poodle chased you down the drive and the postman ran you over with his bicycle. I thought you were dead."

"That blinking Snapper," growled Gordon "I shall have to get my own back on him."

"What is that round you neck and head?" Tushtots enquired, "it looks like a satellite dish, rather like the one on the side of Willi's house."

"Don't be silly," Gordon told him, "it's supposed to stop me biting my stitches."

Gordon painfully lifted his broken leg to show a magnificent set of black stitches on the wound on his tummy. The cats gasped when they saw the vet's needlework.

"Gosh, I bet that hurts," commented Ginger Tompkins, "what's all that wire in your mouth for?"

"I've got a broken jaw as well and this is to put my jaw back into place."

"Really?" Tushtots pondered, "I could have done with those when my jaw was broken, but I had no treatment, which is why my jaw is all crooked now. Can I have your wires when you've finished with them please Gordon, they might put my jaw back in place?"

"Don't be silly," scoffed Willi Whizkas, "it's too late to do anything with your jaw now."

Tushtots sighed. "I bet your operation cost a lot of money, your humans must really love you."

The cats settled carefully on the sofa with Gordon, to pass the time and to take his mind off his injuries they each took a turn in telling Gordon about their adventures. Ginger Tompkins told him all about

Tigaz and how hopelessly he had fallen in love with her. Tushtots related the tale of how he had been shaved and rehomed because he hadn't been loved and wanted, and how he had met Willi Whizkas who had shown him all his favourite places including the mouse under the shed. Willi Whizkas told Gordon all about the party and how he had stolen the trifle and bitten holes in the salmon. The cats laughed riotously, except Gordon who could only let out a feeble chuckle, and even that hurt him. Gordon then told the cats all about an adventure he had when he was much younger, when he lived in a small cottage by a farm.

"The cottage was riddled with mice, my job was to keep the house clear of mice. Now some cats are good at catching mice, and others aren't so good, I'm afraid I was useless. I chased them round and round, up and down the stairs, under the bed, up the curtains and just when I thought I would close my jaws on the little blighters, they always managed to escape. But one day I surpassed myself and brought a mouse back from the pantry to show my humans how efficient I was, but all they did was laugh!"

"Why did they laugh, Gordon?" Willi Whizkas enquired, "you proved yourself to be a mouser."

"Well not quite," confessed Gordon "This one was already caught in a mousetrap!" All four cats fell about giggling as Gordon went on "But one rat I hope to catch is the one who keeps sneaking through my catflap and eating my breakfast!"

Willi Whizkas let out a nervous cough. "Well, I think it's time we were going, there's nothing heals wounds quicker than a good catnap," but before they left they decided that they would have to gang up and teach Snapper a lesson when Gordon was well again.

"More tea vicar? More tea vicar?" Squawked the bird as the boys darted through the catflap, happy to see Gordon home and being looked after.

10 Best Friends

Willi Whizkas had been moping around the garden for days now, things were not quite as they should be, but he couldn't quite put his paw on what was wrong. There were plenty of birds on the bird table, snails slithering across the garden and the gentle hum of bees as they visited the flower beds. He had tired himself out trying to identify what was amiss, so he took a catnap and was having his favourite dream. The little grey mouse would come out from under the shed, stand on his back legs and go "Bleeeeuuuurgh" at Willi Whizkas, then a cat-and-mouse chase followed round and round the garden shed. Willi Whizkas drooled in anticipation of teeth and grey fur meeting at long last. It was at this point that he woke with a start, his dream broken by the realisation that the mouse had been missing for days! He went to investigate the shed, pushing flowers and weeds to one side with his paws. His eyes peered, his nose sniffed but to no avail, there was no sign, not even a squeak of the mouse. If the mouse had gone then where was it? It was unlikely that it had moved to a better home, but if it had been caught and eaten, then by whom? The claw of suspicion pointed firmly at Tushtots. Willi Whizkas had caught him on more than one occasion looking for his mouse. That had to be it, there was no other explanation. Determined to take his revenge he stalked off in search of the suspected culprit. "I'll give him a good hiding," he fumed.

Tushtots was sunning himself in the beetroot patch

when Willi Whizkas pounced, and the fur flew as Willi Whizkas gave Tushtots a jolly good thrashing.

"Stop, stop Wills, what are you doing?" Tushtots screamed, but Willi Whizkas was having none of it as he got round to the business of putting Tushtots firmly in his place.

"You've eaten my mouse you sneak," he growled furiously, "I told you that mouse was mine!"

"Hold on a minute," Tushtots pleaded, "I haven't had your scabby mouse."

"Well, I don't believe you," insisted Willi Whizkas. "A best pal would never eat his best pal's mouse. I'll thank you to stay out of my garden in future." With that he gave Tushtots an almighty thwack across the nose resulting in a blooded scratch, he turned, tail in the air then marched off in a huff.

Tushtots, perplexed by the whole affair went to find a quiet corner and lick his wounds. Over the next few days Willi Whizkas mooched around his garden, never straying far, brooding about his missing mouse. He started to miss Tushtots and he hadn't seen Ginger Tompkins since the quarrel, so to try and lift his spirits he decided to pop over to see him. Ginger Tompkins was sitting on the garden wall playing 'swot the bluebottle' with Tushtots. This had been a favourite game on summer afternoons for Willi Whizkas and Ginger Tompkins before Tushtots had arrived, so Willi Whizkas shouted;

"Hello boys, can I join in?" But Tushtots and Ginger Tompkins turned around and pointedly ignored him. Unbeknown to Willi Whizkas, Tushtots and Ginger Tompkins had been playing together for the past few days, Tushtots had discussed Willi's accusation, and assault, with the other cat. They both considered Willi Whizkas to be out of order taking such drastic action, and had decided they were going to ignore him. Willi

Whizkas shouted to them again, but the only response he got was two angry tails wagging in disapproval over the garden wall. Willi Whizkas could see that his old friend was siding with his new ex-friend, and hissed angrily.

"Oh, I see, you've taken sides with him, well that's cleared that up thank you very much, who needs a mouse-murderer for a friend anyway?" He proudly stuck his tail into the air and stomped back to his own garden, where for a couple more days his sombre mood continued. He was missing his friends, he felt sure they were having adventures without him, he felt thoroughly miserable.

It was a gloomy grey wet day, he'd been turfed out by the humans, who had yet to buy him a catflap. It was too wet to lie under the dripping bushes but he spotted that his humans had accidentally left the shed door open. Getting into the shed was no substitute for a real adventure, but at least there was somewhere dry amongst the jumble of lawn mowers, garden tables and deck chairs for him to curl up and doze the morning away. He found a piece of old carpet and was just about to drift off when his eyes sensed movement, he heard something trickling onto the floor from the shelves.

"Aye aye," thought Willi Whizkas "what's going on here?" He cast a sleepy eye in the direction of a sack of bird seed from which seeds were trickling.

"I wonder what's brought that on, it wasn't doing that when I came in." It didn't take long to find the cause. There in the gloom of the barn was Willi's little grey mouse, its cheeks bulging with seeds, making a swift getaway, disappearing down a knothole in the floor! He couldn't believe his eyes and leapt across the floor to peer through the knothole. It took a few seconds to get used to the dark, but when it did he could just make out a little ball of straw, dried leaves and, of all things, some of Willi's fur all bundled up to make a nest. What he saw next was even more amazing, his little grey mouse had four tiny pink hairless babies, all curled up. The nest was right under the middle of the shed, Willi Whizkas would never have seen it from the outside as it was too dark and too far away from the edge. What's more his paws were too big to poke through the knothole, so once again he had been foiled by the mouse. He watched fascinated for some minutes as the mouse chewed the seeds and looked back defiantly at him.

"What an incredible story this will be to tell Tushtots and Ginger Tompkins," thought the failed mouser, until he remembered that the mouse that he was watching was the very mouse he had accused Tushtots of eating. Willi Whizkas had got a lot of apologising to do, which he wasn't looking forward to at all, as it is never easy to admit you are wrong. He ambled over to Tushtot's house and poked his head through the catflap, having rehearsed in his mind what he was going to say. Tushtots and Ginger Tompkins, in the kitchen window ogling the birds in the garden, greeted Willi Whizkas with stony silence until Tushtots said,

"Come on Ginger we'll have an adventure."

Willi Whizkas hurried to make his apology. "I'm sorry Tushtots," he pleaded, as he began to relate the whole saga, but Tushtots cut him short.

"Best pals don't duff their best pals up before they've checked their facts," at that he jumped down from the window, flipped open the fridge and pulled out an enormous bag of scraps. Willi Whizkas licked his lips and drooled, he knew what was in that bag!

"It's no good you licking your lips, Willi, you're not invited. Come on Ginge, let's take the food upstairs onto the duvet and have a feast."

Willi Whizkas felt well and truly left out as he padded back to his own garden; he was sorry for what he had done to Tushtots, and even sorrier Tushtots didn't want to be his friend any more. All of a sudden Ginger Tompkins crashed through the catflap chasing after him.

"Hang on Willi, old sausage," he panted, "Tushtots was only teaching you a lesson, he knows you were wrong, what's more, he knows that you know you were wrong, so come and join the feast and make up with him." Willi's tail lifted into the air and so did his whiskers! He followed Ginger Tompkins back through the catflap and up the stairs. After all the food had been devoured, paws and whiskers groomed Willi Whizkas apologised once more to Tushtots and explained properly what had happened, after which they all went to Willi's shed so they could see for themselves.

As luck would have it the shed door was still open, so Willi was able to point out the bag of seeds and the trail leading to the knothole.

"See, just as I told you," Willi Whizkas announced,

"So, where's this hole?" Tushtots asked impatiently.

"I think you'll find you're sitting on it!" Willi Whizkas laughed.

"Oh yes, I wondered what the draft was," Tushtots giggled. Willi Whizkas put his eye to the knothole just to make sure that the mouse with her babies were still there, and sure enough a nervous little mouse with black eyes and shiny whiskers stared right back.

"Right Tushtots, you go first, it takes a little while for your eye to get used to the dark."

Ginger Tompkins demanded to have his turn at the knothole. "Let me see, let me see," he begged, pushing the other two aside. He too had never seen a mouse at such close quarters he tested the hole for size with his paw, but had to admit defeat.

"It looks like you mouse is still safe," Ginger Tompkins acknowledged ruefully.

Now everybody had the story straight, apologies were repeated and the cats were friends again.

"Now then," said Tushtots, "you haven't got just one mouse under your shed, if I'm not mistaken when those babies have grown up in a few weeks time there will be five, you can't claim them all for yourself can you? That makes it one mouse each and a couple spare."

Willi Whizkas thought hard about this for a few moments, he decided that it would be best to make a peace offering, despite it being his garden shed and his mice.

"OK", he agreed, "but we must all be honest and fair, if you do catch one, you must show me the tail." By this time the rain had stopped and the sun had come out, there could be no nicer way to end to a day which had started so miserably for Willi Whizkas than with a good roll on the cat mint bush. Willi's eye glazed as he let out a few chirrups and waved his paws in the air. All was well!

11 Tushtot's Big Adventure

Willi Whizkas stretched out on the work surface just enjoying life. The whole day was his, he'd no obligations, except one perhaps. His female human had just put the kettle on and started to give him a good stroke, so he turned over onto his back, stretched all four paws out and let her give him a good tummy tickle, which lasted until the kettle boiled. He wondered if he was going to be fed, he always seemed to wake up hungry, so where was his breakfast? The human turned her attention to Willi Whizkas again and tickled the pink pads on his paws.

"You like that don't you Willi? A bit of pussnatherapy," she laughed, and it was true, he did. She then produced his breakfast, but his usual brand of cat meat was nowhere to be seen, thankfully. Instead he was eating his way through the current special offer at the supermarket, which came with a free bowl decorated with paw prints and a picture of a happy smiling cat. Breakfast finished, it was time to go out into the garden for a good yawn, wash and bottom licking, after which he would be ready to face the day.

He still had a twinge of guilt about the fallout with Tushtots over the mouse, but he thought a really good adventure would heal their wounded friendship. He set off to find Tushtots and run a few suggestions past him, but when he nosed Tushtots' catflap open Tushtots' human looked round from the kitchen sink and told him.

"Hello Mogateer, Tushtots isn't here, last time I saw him he was in the front garden sunning himself." Willi Whizkas gave an appreciative miaow and before long found Tushtots lazing on the family car enjoying the warm morning sunshine. Willi Whizkas jumped onto the bonnet, nearly slipped off, but just managed to get a claw-hold on a windscreen wiper saving himself from an embarrassing tumble.

"Good morning Willi," yawned Tushtots, "come up and join me." Willi Whizkas sat on the sunroof which was not quite as hot as the metal on the car roof.

"We must have an adventure before the summer is over, something which we'll remember when we're shut in on cold winter days. Any ideas Tushtots?"

"Not really," replied Tushtots, "I thought you were the expert at that sort of thing?"

Willi Whizkas looked vacantly into the air for a few moments then asked Tushtots.

"Are you allowed out at night?"

"Oooh, not really sure, the cat flap's never locked, so I assume that my humans will let me come and go as I please, but it's so warm and comfortable on the duvet that I've never really wanted to go out at night."

"There's lots of things that come out at night that you don't see during the day," purred Willi Whizkas excitedly,

"O.K." Tushtots agreed, "if it's a fine evening come and call for me, I'll sit in the kitchen window and wait for you." Which was exactly where Willi Whizkas found Tushtots that night.

"Wake up sleepy head," Willi Whizkas whispered loudly through Tushtots' catflap, "Let's go and have an adventure." The cats set off back through Willi's garden and out onto the road.

"I don't really like roads," Tushtots told Willi Whizkas

as he remembered his broken jaw, the bruises and the other injuries he'd had.

"It'll be OK" Willi Whizkas assured him "trust me." The cats darted across the road and up the gravel path that led to the allotment, their little paw pads crunching noisily on the gravel in the quiet of the night. After a few metres they came across a gate.

"That's not there during the day," Willi Whizkas commented as the cats squeezed underneath and left the sleepy street behind them. The cats marched bravely on, the light from the street lamps faded away and it was almost totally dark. Tushtots wasn't sure if he liked this adventure, he imagined that there was a bogey-cat around every bush just waiting to pounce Tushtots suggested timidly that perhaps they should go back home, but Willi Whizkas wouldn't hear of it.

"We're here to sniff out an adventure," said Willi Whizkas. They could just make out the little allotment sheds, so Willi Whizkas suggested that they go and see what they could find, maybe someone had left a shed door or window open. They approached the first shed cautiously, as they walked up to the door a gruff voice bellowed;

"Who goes there?" The cats sprang up on all four paws, the fur on their backs absolutely rigid.

"It's Willi Whizkas and Tushtots," Willi Whizkas nervously replied

"Come over here where I can see you," the voice commanded, so the two cats slowly inched their way towards the voice. "I knew this adventure was a bad idea," Tushtots hissed.

I'm beginning to think you're right," Willi Whizkas agreed.

"A little closer if you don't mind," the voice continued. Suddenly Ginger Tompkins sprang from behind a bush, laughing his whiskers off. The two trembling cats almost fainted with shock which made Ginger Tompkins laugh even more.

"You nearly scared us to death!" Willi Whizkas scolded.

"I still want to go home," pleaded Tushtots, "I shouldn't have listened to you Willi, I could be tucked up on the duvet asleep with my humans." Willi Whizkas asked how it was that Ginger Tompkins happened to be at the allotments.

"I often come here if I have trouble sleeping, there's always something going on," he told them. Just then there was a loud shriek followed by a "Who who whoooo"

"See what I mean? That's an owl, just in case you didn't know."

"Birds don't fly at night," retorted Tushtots.

"Owls do," Ginger Tompkins stated authoritatively, "they have enormous eyes, enormous ears and they can catch mice better than any cat. I've spent many a night on top of a shed just watching them in the moonlight."

The cats spent half an hour or so nosing around the allotment sheds, but they were all securely locked and the only thing they did find of interest was a huge hedgehog crunching a very large snail.

"That's disgusting," said Tushtots, "how can anyone eat one of those slimy things?" All three cats pulled a face at the prospect at having to eat a snail! Then Ginger Tompkins had a bright idea.

"What about the haunted house? There's always the haunted house." Never in his wildest dreams did he think that the other two would want to go. Ginger Tompkins had always been too scared, even in the company of Thugsby the neighbourhood alley cat who was renowned for being fearless.

"O.K." replied Willi Whizkas, "lead on." After dodging

through clumps of rhubarb, patches of potatoes and sets of stinky onions they came to a tall hedge through which they could just make out a large red roof under which the windows were all smashed.

"What is this place?" Tushtots asked, not sure if this was going to be a good idea after all.

"Well, Thugsby told me it once belonged to an old lady who used to feed all the stray cats in the area, that's how he knew about it. She would bathe poorly eyes, put ear drops into poorly ears and cuddled cats who were sad."

"What happened to her?" Willi Whizkas enquired, wanting to know more.

"Well," Ginger Tompkins went on, "the story goes that she died of old age, alone in the house and no-one found her for days. They say that her ghost still haunts the house and garden calling for stray cats."

"But will we be all right, after all we're not stray cats?" Tushtots wondered.

"Not sure old fruit," answered Ginger Tompkins, "I've not known of any cat who's visited since she passed away."

"Perhaps we shouldn't go in?" Willi Whizkas whispered, getting cold paws at the thought of coming nose to face with a ghost.

"But wouldn't it make a fantastic adventure if we did see the ghost and lived to tell the tale?" Ginger Tompkins suggested.

The cats crept as quietly as they could through the overgrown garden.

"It's like a jungle here," whispered Tushtots. Ginger Tompkins and Willi Whizkas let out a loud "Shush!".

The house was huge and very forbidding, most of the windows were broken and the back door banged on its hinges. Just then the owl from the allotment let out an eerie hoot which frightened the cats even more!

"Who's going to be first in?" Ginger Tompkins asked shakily,

"Well, I'm going to follow you Ginge," said Willi Whizkas.

"And I'm following you Willi," stated Tushtots.

"And I'm following Tushtots," whispered Ginger Tompkins.

"So that makes you first, Willi," declared Ginger Tompkins and Tushtots together. Willi Whizkas scratched his head in puzzlement for a few seconds.

"Come on Willi," Tushtots encouraged him, "you wanted an adventure." All three of them pushed at the creaking door then carefully padded inside. The interior was terrifyingly dark except for a shaft of moonlight that lit the staircase via a gaping hole in the roof.

"Shall we go up?" Willi Whizkas asked, silently the cats began to climb the stairs. There was dust and dirt everywhere and the staircase began to creak and groan with every step the brave cats took as they sought out the old lady's ghost. Several doors led off the top of the landing and they weren't sure which door to open first.

"Try the end door," ventured Tushtots just as a swarm of large black beetles scurried out from under a carpet then disappeared into the darkness. The door was just open enough for Willi Whizkas to squeeze through, he was immediately entangled in a dusty old spider's web full of dried-up dead flies, so he shot back and cleaned the sticky residue off his face and whiskers.

"I think you had better go first this time Ginge," muttered Willi Whizkas through a mouth full of cobweb.

Ginger Tompkins reluctantly agreed, and the trembling trio inched forwards. They could hear high-pitched squeaks coming from the ceiling and soon discovered dozens of black bats hanging from the crumbling plaster. Willi Whizkas couldn't hold back a sneeze that the cobweb had caused any longer and let out a mighty "A . . . CHOO.".

The bats took off like a black cloud, dive-bombing the cats as they went, then in an instant they all flew out of a broken window. The cats fled back to the landing in fright, tripping over some empty glass bottles which rolled through the bannister and crashed noisily down the stairs. Suddenly a large door in the middle of the landing flew open and a huge white spectre staggered towards the terrified cats, who hurtled down the stairs ending up in a dusty heap at the bottom. Without pausing to catch breath they raced into the garden, fleeing the heavy footsteps they could hear behind them. Just then a loud human voice bellowed.

"Who's there? Show yourself!"

The cats didn't stop, they leapt through the tangled undergrowth, squeezed through the hedge then ran and ran until they got safely back to Willi's garden. They were all filthy dirty, covered in dust and cobwebs, and shaking with fear.

"I'm off home," panted Tushtots, "back to the safety of my duvet."

Me too!!" Ginger Tompkins whispered.

"What about me?" Willi Whizkas wailed, "I'm the only one without a catflap, I can't get in!" But the other two had scarpered and left him. He mewed and yowled at his back door for what seemed an eternity until one of his humans opened the door and saw what a state he was in.

"What's up with you Willi? It looks like you've seen a ghost!!"

A couple of days later Stinker of the yard was doing his rounds, he found all three cats sunbathing in Tushtots garden.

"Hello Stinker, what brings you here?" Willi Whizkas asked.

"I'm just here to let you boys know that I've got a spot of bother on my patch. There's a story going round that an old human tramp is sleeping rough in the area. You can't miss him, he wears a long white coat, so keep 'em peeled as they say!"

"That could be who we saw at the house," whispered Tushtots

"No," said Willi Whizkas knowledgeably, "What we saw was a real ghost!"

12 Gordon's Revenge

Willi Whizkas and Ginger Tompkins were at a loose end one morning, after they'd had breakfast, washed, then dug the required holes in the vegetable patch.

"Let's go for a different sort of walk," suggested Willi Whizkas, never short of an idea. "Let's stroll along the fence tops and survey the neighbourhood." So off they went. Every garden they passed they peered into just to see what was doing. Birds like to stand on fence tops too, but they flew off in droves as the cats approached. Suddenly Willi Whizkas realised where he was. He froze and said in a hushed voice;

"You know who's house is next don't you, Gingey?"

"I think you may have to remind me old thing," replied Ginger Tompkins.

"This is where Snapper the poodle lives." Snapper was the nasty poodle who caused Gordon's awful accident, and they had all agreed that Snapper must be taught a lesson. So with this in mind the two cats had a good look round Snapper's garden from the safety of his fence, which was just too high for Snapper to jump up and reach them. The fence appeared to have no holes anywhere, so how was Snapper getting out?

"He must be let out through the front door when he takes himself for a walk," mused Willi Whizkas. Just as they were about to give up Snapper came racing out into the garden from his kennel, so the cats made a reasonably dignified retreat. When they got back to Willi's garden they decided they'd go and report to Gordon, collecting Tushtots on the way. Gordon still had a noticeable limp, but the fur was growing nicely on his tummy where the stitches had been removed. He was sitting on the doorstep watching the world go by when the three Mogateers trotted up the drive. The four cats tried to come up with a master plan, but nothing came to mind, so Willi Whizkas asked if they could go into Gordon's house and see the bird in the cage.

"Only on one condition, it's my pal now, so you don't jump up and frighten him. While I've been recovering, I've taught him how to miaow!" They all trooped in through Gordon's catflap into the kitchen, where Willi Whizkas spotted a bowl of half-eaten cat meat.

"Do you not like your food Gordon?" Willi enquired.

"No," he replied, "it's some awful stuff that's been on offer at the supermarket, as for that free dish with the paw prints and the smiling cat on it, I simply refuse to eat from it."

"I could finish it off for you Gordon," volunteered Willi Whizkas.

"No, leave it there, it's bait, I've still not caught the blighter who creeps in and helps himself." Willi Whizkas Ginger Tompkins and Tushtots looked at each other and smirked.

The bird in the cage was magnificent as ever, eyeing them up as they pushed their way into the room.

"Squawk, squawk where's Gordon? Miaow!" However, their attention quickly passed from the bird to a large bowl on the table with two huge goldfish in it!! The humans had bought it for Gordon to take his mind off his injuries. Willi Whizkas bounded over to the sideboard and pressed an eye up against the glass.

"You'll not catch them," sighed Gordon gloomily, "the humans put a net over the bowl when they caught me with a paw in the water. Apparently you're just supposed to watch them go round and round blowing bubbles at each other."

As the fish came near to the glass they were greatly magnified, Willi Whizkas couldn't believe how huge they were, but as soon as they swam away, they went quite small again. There was something mesmerising about watching the fish that gave him inspiration for his master plan. They all huddled on the sofa and Willi Whizkas told them what he had in mind. After they had discussed the plan, Gordon decided that he wasn't quite fit enough to take part, but he would come and watch the others. They all agreed that Sunday evening, when humans go to bed early because they have to be up for work on Monday, would be the ideal time. So it was on Sunday evening that they walked along the garden fences just as Willi Whizkas and Ginger Tompkins had done a few days previously. The plan was fairly simple, but it involved precise timing, and the cats' ability to jump on and off the fence before Snapper could sink his fearsome teeth into their backsides. Willi Whizkas took one side of the garden, Tushtots the other and Ginger Tompkins the bottom. Gordon sat on a branch of an overhanging tree out of everyone's way. As planned, Gordon let out a loud yowl, as if a cat fight was about to take place.

Snapper came racing out of his kennel barking furiously, at which Willi Whizkas jumped off the fence into the garden. This caught Snapper's eye and he chased after him, but just as he was about to catch Willi Whizkas, Ginger Tompkins jumped off the fence then ran across the garden in the direction Willi Whizkas had just come from. Snapper didn't know which way to turn, who to chase, or who to bark at! Tushtots now jumped from his section of the fence, raced up to

Snapper's kennel and leapt onto the coal house behind it. Snapper went berserk, the more the cats jumped on and off the fence, the louder Snapper barked and the more confused he became. Meanwhile Gordon watched the 'entertainment' laughing his whiskers off!

After a few minutes of frantic barking, a neighbour's bedroom window opened, a human shouted down to Snapper to be quiet, then an old slipper was thrown in his direction. One by one further bedroom lights came on, windows opened and angry shouts were directed at Snapper, until finally his owner came out, dragged him into the kitchen and gave him a good telling-off. The cats regrouped, laughing so much so that Gordon's recently mended jaw began to ache. They had enjoyed the evening, and decided to repeat the exercise the following week. Sure enough, just like the first time Snapper dashed round and round barking and yelping for all he was worth, thoroughly annoying the neighbours. On the third Sunday they tried again, but Snapper was nowhere to be seen. Willi Whizkas even padded bravely up to Snapper's kennel, to no avail.

Snapper was definitely not around, so there followed a quick discussion as to what may have happened to him. Gordon thought he may just have been kept inside, Ginger Tompkins thought he had been sent to the naughty dogs home, while Tushtots thought that he'd been rehomed then Willi Whizkas joked that Snapper may have been taken into police custody! Not knowing what had happened to Snapper, the cats sloped off home, disappointed at missing their fun.

The following morning the cats met up at Gordon's house, they sat in the bay window which overlooked the street. This was a good vantage point, because most days Snapper would walk by sniffing the flowers and weeing up the lampposts as he took himself for a walk around the neighbourhood. They watched and waited but there was no sign of Snapper.

"Perhaps he's had an accident," said Gordon, "it wouldn't be the first accident in the street would it?" But there was no word of Snapper until Stinker of the Yard caught up with them a couple of days later as they were chasing hover flies in Ginger Tompkins' garden.

"Hello Stinker," called Willi Whizkas, "we've not seen you around for a while."

"No, my patch has been very quiet just recently, with one notable exception."

"What's that?" Willi Whizkas wondered.

"Well," Stinker replied, "it turns out that one Parisienne Bouffant Curly Kews, known to his friends as Snapper, although I have yet to receive any evidence that he has any friends, has had a restraining order placed upon him by the local magistrate.".

"What does that mean?" Ginger Tompkins asked.

"They glue his paws to the floor!" Willi Whizkas laughed.

"It means that he now has a criminal record sir, and he has been bound over to keep the peace."

"Does that mean he has been tied up as well?"

"No, Master Willi," replied Stinker with authority, "it means that he must be muzzled, kept on a lead and supervised by a human whenever he leaves the premise of his abode. Now as you may or not know, Snapper's human is housebound and there have been no volunteers to take him for walks due to all the disturbances he has caused, in particular the incident with the postman and your good self Gordon. Add to that all the yapping he has been doing, keeping the humans awake and causing a general nuisance, and something had to be done. I am pleased to inform you that justice has been served in bringing the young tear away to account. Well, criminals to catch and all that, a police-cats work is never done," and with that Stinker of the Yard marched smartly down the road.

"To hear him speak you wouldn't think he was just the police station mouser," chortled Tushtots as the nasty smell that always accompanied Stinker disappeared round the corner with him.

"Well," commented Willi Whizkas, "it looks like my plan worked after all. Snapper's grounded and muzzled, Gordon's almost fit and well, I think we all deserve a jolly good nap." The cats returned to their own gardens and dozed away the afternoon.

A week or so later Gordon was tired of listening to the bird in the cage telling him that he loved him and miaowing like a cat. He was also tired of watching the goldfish swimming round and round so he went to sit in his front garden and watch the world go by. Just then who should come around the corner but the postman, on foot, accompanied by none other than a muzzled and restrained Snapper on the end of a shiny new red lead!!

"Good morning Parisienne Bouffant Curly Kews," shouted a highly satisfied Gordon, and If dogs could understand what cats say, Snapper would have turned red with embarrassment!

13 Nothing to Crow About

It was a fine sunny morning and Willi Whizkas was having a roll on his catnip patch. At times like this he always ended up on his back with his legs in the air with a glazed expression on his silly face, it was such bliss. He wasn't sure how long he lay there writhing in ecstasy, but when he came to his senses, he noticed something that he hadn't seen before, or if he had seen it he hadn't noticed it. The tall oak tree in the garden next to Tushtots' was almost in full leaf, but through a small gap in the leaves he spotted a birds nest. This was no ordinary birds nest, it was huge, made of lots of twigs all jumbled together, sticking to a branch near the top of the tree. Willi Whizkas looked with even closer interest when he saw the small head of a baby crow peering over the edge. Willi's eyes were fixed on the nest for some moments as he wondered about the possibility of succulent baby crow for lunch. It was no easy task to climb an oak tree, it would be even more difficult to avoid the attentions of the parent crows, whose large black beaks could easily have his eye out if he wasn't careful. He decided to call on Ginger Tompkins to see what he knew about the nest and it's appetising baby crow.

"You've been on the cat mint again haven't you old fruit," sniffed Ginger Tompkins.

"It sort of sets me up for the day," Willi Whizkas replied, "I wouldn't swap my catnip patch for anything."

"What about a catflap?" Ginger Tompkins retorted smugly. Willi Whizkas wasn't sure if he would rather have his cat mint patch or a catflap.

"Never mind that, there are more important things to discuss. What do you know about that" he snapped, pointing a claw in the direction of the nest. Ginger Tompkins wasn't quite sure what Willi Whizkas was talking about so they climbed onto the garage roof to get a better look.

"Do you know, I never noticed that," gasped Ginger Tompkins in astonishment as he watched the baby crow's black eyes peeping down at them. "Have you ever tackled a crow, old thing? They're not as easy as they look, they've got huge wings and a massive beak, it's not like a run of the mill sparrow!"

"Well I'm going to give it a go, how easy do you think that tree is going to be to climb?"

"Mmmm, tricky one that old chap. The first half looks OK, but the branches thin out when you get near the top, but that's exactly where the nest is." Willi Whizkas looked at the tree, as he rehearsed in his mind the route up to the nest, he could almost feel the shiny black feathers in his grasp.

"Well, good luck old sausage if you're going to have a go at it, but watch out for its parents, they're not to be tangled with."

Willi Whizkas sprang into the tree and began his ascent.

"Go on Willi old chap, you've got a long way to go yet," encouraged Ginger Tompkins as Willi Whizkas climbed. The rough bark could have been made for a cat, anyway Willi had made a special effort to sharpen his claws on the back of the sofa just that morning!

By now he was at the halfway stage, he felt quite dizzy as he looked down. He could see that Ginger Tompkins had now been joined by Tushtots, their furry faces looking up in admiration, but he was beginning to think that this wasn't such a good idea after all. There was still quite a way to go, he had to negotiate some tricky bits with no branches to rest on. By now his tummy was rumbling. With one huge effort he spread his paws out round the tree-trunk and climbed like a squirrel. He was now exactly where he wanted to be, beside the nest. The baby crow looked nervously at him and let out a couple of squeaks, now all Willi Whizkas had to do was inch along to grab his prize. He started to paw along carefully, but it wasn't going to be easy, with the branch swaying in the breeze. Alas, at that precise moment the baby crow's dad arrived with a beak full of worms, it didn't take him long to spot Willi Whizkas and start to 'caw, caw, caw' before flying at him in a rage.

Willi Whizkas could hear the beat of wings and felt the air whoosh around him as the crow dive-bombed him. He almost lost balance and had to cling on for dear life as the crow, now joined by his wife, fought for the life of their offspring There was such a commotion of flapping wings and 'caw, caw caws' that humans in the houses below came out to see what the noise was all about. Ginger Tompkins and Tushtots looked up at Willi Whizkas, fearful of what might happen, wondering exactly how many of his nine lives Willi Whizkas had left.

"Not many," mused Ginger Tompkins thoughtfully, "the scrapes he's got himself into over the past couple of years!"

Meanwhile, Willi Whizkas was absolutely petrified. The dive-bombing crows would have been enough to contend with on the ground, but on top of a tree they were even more scary, what was he to do? He was too scared to go up or down, making a grab for the baby crow was out of the question. He edged his way into a fork in the branches and clung on for dear life. Meanwhile the humans had gathered at the bottom of the oak tree, Tushtots and Ginger Tompkins had climbed onto the garage to get a ringside view.

"Whose is that cat?" One of the humans asked.

"He hangs around with my Ginger," Ginger Tompkins' human replied "his name's Willi Whizkas and he's always up to no good. I'm glad he's not my cat!"

"Well we'd better go and get his owner," suggested another human, but they were already on their way, having heard the commotion. By now the crows had settled down a bit and were nursing their baby on the nest, while Willi Whizkas remained paralysed with fear. Discussions ensued about contacting the R.S.P.C.A. or the fire brigade, or even getting some ladders.

"I'll just get his cat meat plate and give it a tap," one of his humans suggested, "he's a greedy cat he always comes when food is in the offing. I'll just leave a plate of meat under the tree, he'll come down when he's ready." But Willi Whizkas didn't and the humans, thinking that they may be making him nervous, dispersed. Ginger Tompkins and Tushtots kept vigil as the light faded.

"He's not coming down," stated Ginger Tompkins "and it's a shame to let that food go to waste." So Ginger Tompkins and Tushtots polished it off for him. They miaowed up at Willi Whizkas, but the only response they got was a pathetic little mew.

Eventually Ginger Tompkins and Tushtots made their way home, Willi Whizkas was left all alone with the watchful stares of the crows, the rustling leaves and the creaking branches. He dare not loosen his grip, even for an instant, so he had to try and stay awake all night, which was unheard of as far as Willi Whizkas was concerned. The only thing that helped keep him awake was the scary shrieks from the owl in the allotment, but then it started to rain and the wind got up, so sleep became impossible anyway. By morning he was thoroughly wet and miserable, the ground was still a long way down. Ginger Tompkins and Tushtots, who had had a very comfortable night and a pleasant breakfast, were up early to see what Willi Whizkas was going to do next.

"I can't believe he's still up there," commented Tushtots, "I thought he would have climbed down or fallen by now." It wasn't till later in the morning that Willi's humans came to make a check on him. Around midday, the rattling of cat meat saucers and crunchy cat biscuits having failed, the fire brigade arrived with several long ladders along with a man from the R.S.P.C.A. with a long pole with a noose on the end of it. Tushtots and Ginger Tompkins took up position on the garage roof and watched with interest as Willi's rescue got under way. Several of the ladders were connected together, then a brave fireman climbed up calling "puss, puss, puss,"

"There they go again, these humans," said Tushtots, "they think every cat in the world is called 'Puss!"

The ladder creaked and groaned under the weight of the fireman, a wide-eyed Willi Whizkas seemed to be even more frightened by the prospect of a rescue than being stuck in the tree. When the fireman was within arm's reach he put out a hand covered in a scratch and bite-proof glove towards Willi Whizkas, who panicked and climbed even higher up the tree, causing the crows to fly round the tree 'cawing' loudly. The fireman went down to the bottom of the ladder then returned with the pole with the noose on it.

"Why don't they just squirt him out with the water hose?" Tushtots asked excitedly.

"Yeah, and catch him with a net as he falls," laughed Ginger Tompkins, but this was no laughing matter. Willi Whizkas was a very long way up a very big tree. The fireman was now as high as the ladder would take him, but Willi Whizkas had nowhere else to go. After several attempts Willi Whizkas was caught around the neck with the noose then unceremoniously brought down, clawing and spitting at his rescuer. All the humans who were on the ground watching let out a gasp and applauded the fireman, who posed for a photo for the local paper with a very embarrassed and ungrateful Willi Whizkas.

"That's another of your lives gone Willi," scolded one of his humans "Perhaps you'll learn to be a good lap-cat one of these days," with that he was scooped up and taken home for a good feed. Gordon, who had not been part of this latest adventure, asked Tushtots what on earth had been going on, so Tushtots told him all about the baby crow and how easy Willi Whizkas thought it would be to shimmy up the tree and catch his own lunch.

"But everyone knows that crows are an acquired taste," Tushtots went on, "and he wouldn't have enjoyed it had he been successful, there's much nicer meat on a sparrow or a mouse!"

14 Mouse-knapped!!

Breakfast time at Willi's house was usually routine, but one day his male human proudly unpacked a new gadget, plugged it in, switched it on and then the female human put some bread into the top of it. Willi Whizkas looked on from the safety of the far end of the work surface with some interest, as it is well known that cats are curious, nosy creatures. As the humans observed the new contraption Willi Whizkas took a few paces nearer himself.

"Not too close now Willi," warned the female human as she leant over the gadget peering into the slots which were now glowing a bright orange. Willi's nose twitched as he caught the scent of something which was decidedly too hot. As a wisp of blue/grey smoke rose slowly towards the ceiling, the new device ejected two blackened pieces of bread with such force that Willi Whizkas shot off the work surface in panic then ran to the kitchen door for safety. Not to be put off, his humans adjusted the gadget then repeated the process which was all very entertaining, but it wasn't putting cat meat into Willi's dish, so he let out a few miaows and rubbed round the female human's legs for attention.

"Yes, you're next Willi," she comforted him "just as soon as we can get this toaster to work." After his breakfast he pottered into the garden where to his shock and horror there on the lawn lay the dead body of a mouse! It was his mouse. Now what he didn't know was that mice only live for a couple of years at best, it could well have died of old age, but he immediately suspected foul play!

Tushtots and Ginger Tompkins knew the rules about the mouse, they certainly wouldn't have left the evidence for him to find so easily. If the humans were to find it he was almost certain to get the blame, so he took the mouse in his mouth and trotted round to the back of the shed where he dug a shallow hole and buried it. Later he rounded up Tushtots and Ginger Tompkins then proceeded to exhume the little corpse as the other two looked on in astonishment.

"Well it wasn't me," snorted Tushtots defensively.

"And it certainly wasn't me!" Sniffed Ginger Tompkins, "I prefer my meat without fur these days thank you." The three of them took it in turns to sniff the dead mouse and give it a little pat with a paw.

"So," asked Willi Whizkas "Who's nobbled my mouse?"

"I don't think you ought to bother Stinker of the Yard," giggled Tushtots "he'd probably polish off the evidence!"

"Well," announced Ginger Tompkins, "there's nothing for it, we'll have to conduct our own investigation," so the cats retired to Tushtots' duvet where they picked a few knots out of their fur while they pondered.

"It must have been a well-fed cat," commented Tushtots logically, "A hungry cat would have eaten it."

"Well that could be any one of the three of us, we're all a bit porky these days," laughed Willi Whizkas.

"I suppose it could have been a stranger," commented Ginger Tompkins.

"Well I know what Stinker of the Yard would say," announced Tushtots with a flash of inspiration.

"And what's that?" Demanded the other two in unison.

"The criminal always returns to the scene of the crime," grinned Tushtots "I bet whoever nobbled your mouse will come back to look for it, and for any other mice that might be had."

"Do you know, I think you're right," Willi agreed

"Well," said Ginger Tompkins, "there's only one thing for it Willi old boy, you'll have to sit up all night and keep watch."

"On my own?"

"Well it's you that's minus a mouse old chap," Ginger Tompkins pointed out, "and to be honest we've all had enough grief over that mouse on and off."

"That's true," agreed Tushtots, remembering the fight he'd had with Willi Whizkas.

Willi Whizkas decided that the best view of the garden was from the kitchen window, and since he didn't fancy staying out all night, particularly as it looked like it was going to be a damp evening, he shot straight inside as soon as the humans got home from work. The humans didn't mind him sitting in the kitchen window, as long as his paws were clean and he didn't climb over dishes in the sink after he'd used his litter tray.

It was a long evening sitting on the cold tiles on the windowsill, he was tempted to slope back to the warmth and comfort of the work surface over the fridge, but then the female human sat him on her knee and gave him a vigorous stroking. Willi Whizkas did what he always did when he was forced to sit on a lap, he dug his claws into her knee and broke wind silently, as only cats can. In no time at all he was put back on the windowsill and a liberal amount of air freshener was sprayed around him.

"You're a bad cat Will," he was told sternly. "You don't deserve a nice home!" Willi couldn't have cared less, his thoughts were still on the phantom mousenobbler. It was getting quite dark by now and he was starting to feel drowsy. He tried to make full use of his excellent night vision but there was nothing to see, his eyes soon became tired staring at the same spot. Almost nodding off, he banged his nose on the window, which startled him somewhat, but still nothing moved in the garden, and it was now well after midnight. The house was in darkness, his humans were upstairs snoring, he was just about to give up when something caught his eye. Was it a bush quivering in the wind? Was it a branch? A hedgehog? His ears pricked up, and he stared until his eyes burned. There was a cat in his garden, one he hadn't seen in his garden before, but one he knew, all the same. Thugsby the alley cat, who used to be looked after by the old lady at the house which Willi Whizkas knew without a doubt to be haunted. Thugsby went round the back of the shed out of Willi's sight only to reappear moments later with something in his mouth. Willi Whizkas let out a growl.

"The swine has got my mouse!" He cursed under his breath as Thugsby melted into the night. Willi Whizkas didn't wait for breakfast the following morning, He miaowed and pawed at the back door until for the sake of peace and quiet he was ejected into the garden, whereupon he pelted across the lawn to the shed. There was the hole, missing its mouse.

" It's gone, it was that Thugsby that swiped it!" Willi Whizkas told Tushtots and Ginger Tompkins later

"Well what are you going to do about it old chap?" Ginger Tompkins asked.

"Not much I can do," moaned Willi Whizkas miserably. "What's gone is gone."

"Still it went to a deserving tummy," commented Tushtots

"Well I think you should have it out with him old thing," insisted Ginger Tompkins, "you can't go around pinching another cat's mouse, what would happen if we all started doing that?"

"You're right," growled Willi Whizkas, "let's go and confront the mouse-murderer!" So the three of them set off for the haunted house. It didn't take long to find Thugsby, who was washing his paws and whiskers having just polished off a piece of foul-smelling mouldy beefburger. Thugsby, surprised to see the three of them, stood up, arched his back and let out a warning hiss. Thugsby's coat was filthy, his face scratched, his ears nicked and he was painfully thin, with a dry and crusty nose. Willi Whizkas had never seen such a shabby cat, but he was still set on having it out with him. Thugsby then recognised Ginger Tompkins.

"Hello Gingey," called Thugsby cheerfully "is this your gang?"

"I suppose so," replied Ginger Tompkins. "It's nice to see you again Thugs, how's tricks?"

"Not too good I'm afraid, since the old lady passed away us old strays have hit on hard times. Nobody feeds us now, so we have to fight for what food we can find."

"Talking about finding food," Willi Whizkas butted in aggressively,

"Not now Willi," hissed Tushtots, "let him continue." Thugsby told them how he envied the three of them with their nice warm comfortable homes and humans who loved them Then he mentioned how quite by chance he had come upon a dead mouse in a shallow hole behind a shed. Willi's mouth gaped in astonishment.

"You mean you didn't kill the mouse yourself?"

"Oh no," confirmed Thugsby "I'm much too old and stiff in my joints to chase around after mice. I think it had died of old age, it would have been dead for a day or so when I found it." Willi Whizkas was now starting to feel very guilty as Thugsby was more in need of the mouse than he would ever be.

"You could do with a decent feed and a new home," observed Tushtots.

"I know," agreed Thugsby sadly, "but older cats find it difficult to get rehomed, it's cute kittens that stand the best chance. I would kill for a human to love and a lap to sit on." Willi Whizkas then hit on one of his master plans.

"Meet me tomorrow morning where you found the mouse, and I'll show you where you can always get a half-eaten breakfast if you don't mind it being a bit crusty round the edges."

"That would be marvellous," drooled Thugsby. The following morning he turned up at the shed.

"Is this your garden?" Thugsby asked Willi Whizkas

"Yes it is," confirmed Willi Whizkas, " and that was my mouse that you ate."

"I am sorry," whispered Thugsby "I had no idea."

"Never mind," Willi Whizkas told him, "let's show you where you can get a free feed."

On the way to Gordon's house, Willi Whizkas filled him in about Gordon, his terrible accident, the bird in the cage and most importantly how Gordon never ate all of his breakfast. From now on Thugsby was to have first refusal of Gordon's leftovers. Thugsby thanked Willi Whizkas, he cautiously nosed open the catflap and disappeared inside, where he ate a hearty breakfast. Willi Whizkas felt the inner glow of a job well done!

15 New Neighbours

When the kitchen door opened one bright new morning Tushtots and Ginger Tompkins were already waiting in the garden for Willi Whizkas, warming their noses in the early morning sun.

"Spot of news for you old chap," Ginger Tompkins informed him.

"What's that?" Willi Whizkas asked,

"I think you're going to have new human neighbours."

"How do you know?"

"Well there's a huge lorry parked outside the house, and there's a human with brown overalls carrying things from the house and packing them away in the removal van."

"Can't say as I've noticed," sniffed Willi Whizkas, "let's cross over to Gordon's where we might get a better view." As they crossed the road they spotted Gordon sitting in his front room window watching the proceedings. Gordon nodded to them to come in, so the three cats nosed through the cat flap, only to be serenaded by the bird in the cage with a chorus of "Love you Gordon, Love you Gordon miaow." The cats padded into the front room, jumped onto the window ledge to join Gordon, and the four of then stared across at the removal van, wondering what sort of family would be moving in. Willi Whizkas was glad that the current family were going as they'd never liked him, always banging the window at him when he dug holes in their garden, coming out to shoo him away when he stalked birds on their lawn, and leaving nasty smelling powder along the flower borders. Somehow he never felt welcome there. Gordon took advantage of this unlikely assembly of neighbourhood cats to inform them about his disappearing breakfasts.

"Really?" Willi Whizkas smirked, trying to look surprised.

"Yes," Gordon went on "these last few days, as soon as my back is turned some sneaky blighter has been snaffling my breakfast. I just caught sight of a tail snaking out of my catflap only this morning. I want to see the tips of your tails, the one I saw this morning had a white tip to it," so one-by-one the cats flourished their tails in Gordon's direction.

"Just the tail will do Willi," Gordon told Willi Whizkas who was showing rather more than his tail, and after a close examination Gordon ruled them out one by one.

"Well thank you for that," said Gordon, "I didn't think a friend would snaffle a pal's breakfast." Tushtots and Ginger Tompkins were surprised that Willi Whizkas wasn't the culprit, as they knew for a fact he frequently stole Gordon's breakfast.

"So who do you suspect then?" Tushtots enquired puzzled.

"Probably a total stranger," suggested Willi Whizkas "look, the van's leaving!"

"The house is empty now," observed Tushtots "Perhaps we should go over and have a good look round without the risk of being booted out."

" I'll leave you boys to it," yawned Gordon, "I'm going to sit in the kitchen window and see if the phantom meat muncher shows his face." The troublesome trio of toms filed across the road to the now empty house, marching up the drive as if they owned the place. Ginger Tompkins jumped up onto the kitchen windowsill and peered inside, observing as he did so.

"Looks like they've gone all right, the place is empty." The three cats spent a happy half-hour just nosing around, enjoying being free to roam. They hadn't quite finished surveying the property when they were disturbed by the squeal of brakes and a clattering engine.

"Looks like your new neighbours have arrived already old chap," announced Ginger Tompkins.

"Are you sure it's not the old family coming back?" Willi Whizkas asked anxiously.

"No, I don't think so," Tushtots commented as through the gate and up the drive strode a man, a woman and a young girl.

"Children!" Willi Whizkas gasped in horror

"What's wrong with children?" Tushtots asked.

"Bit of a mixed blessing in my view," moaned Willi Whizkas, "sometimes they can be very nice, but other times they pick you up all wrong, or tease you until you have to hiss at them, plus they expect you to keep chasing endless pieces of paper and wool across the carpet."

"How do you know all this? Your humans haven't got any children," Tushtots pointed out.

"No but I spent a week with their relatives and they have three children. I never thought I would get home alive."

"Well there's only one child, I'm sure you'll cope old boy," laughed Ginger Tomkins.

From the safety of the garden the cats watched the new family explore their new home. The little girl looked out of a window and spotted the cats. Smiling, she gave them a little wave.

"She seems tame enough," commented Tushtots.

"You could be right here, though you can never really tell." Ginger Tompkins commented, "I got shut in a broom cupboard once by a child and it took two days for the humans to find me." There wasn't much else to do so the cats contented themselves watching the comings and goings as piece by piece the empty house became someone's new home. Then the little girl came running down the garden to where the cats were lazing, causing all three of them to scarper in different directions. Willi Whizkas shot back into his own garden, Tushtots went over the fence and Ginger Tompkins melted into the bushes. The little girl began to call.

"Puss, puss puss,"

"Here we go again," thought Willi Whizkas, "that cat called Puss must have got around a bit for every human to know his name." The little girl disappeared back into the kitchen then came back again a few minutes later clutching a nice piece of lean chicken. Willi Whizkas sniffed the air excitedly as the tender slice of chicken was waved in his direction. As he had missed out on his breakfast at Gordon's he decided that the little girl's offering was worth investigating. He poked his head through the hedge trying to reach the chicken, but the little girl kept backing away just as he got within claw's reach. Ginger Tompkins looked on from under the bushes, he couldn't believe that Willi Whizkas could be so easily tempted, especially as he had not long since spoken of his dislike of children. The little girl sat down and proceeded to feed Willi Whizkas the chicken tiny pieces at a time, dangling tasty morsels above his head so that he had to stand on his back legs and beg for it. Soon all the chicken had gone, so the little girl reached out and started to stroke him. Tushtots, who was now back sitting on the fence smiled with approval, it was nice to see Willi Whizkas had made a new friend. As the afternoon turned into early evening a small white van drew up onto the drive, a man got out carrying a large wooden box which he put down behind the garage. Willi Whizkas watched with some interest, why weren't they taking it into the house with all the furniture? Why were they leaving this wardrobe-sized box in the garden where it would surely get wet? It was most peculiar, even Tushtots had to agree, they had never seen anything like it. When the humans disappeared the cats went to investigate. Tushtots jumped on top of it.

"It's got a proper roof," he shouted down, "it looks like it's supposed to be outside." Willi Whizkas peered in through the chicken wire at the side, his nose twitched as he caught a whiff, the likes of which he had never smelt before.

"Pooh, come and have a niff of this, smells like something has died in there!" But no matter how much they looked and sniffed the purpose of the construction defeated them. Shortly afterwards the new family approached the wooden box, armed with what appeared to be a cat basket. The three friends darted under the bushes and looked on in amazement as not a cat, but a beautiful long haired lop-eared rabbit emerged from the basket. A door in the box was opened and the rabbit placed inside, then the door was smartly closed behind it. The three of them stared in astonishment.

"What on earth is that?" Willi Whizkas asked.

"It's neither a cat not a dog," said Tushtots, unable to identify the creature.

"You boys have led sheltered lives," laughed Ginger Tompkins, "everyone knows, apart from you two apparently, that thing is a rabbit."

"A rabbit?!" Willi Whizkas repeated, "What do rabbits do?"

"Well old things," Ginger Tompkins started with an air of authority "they sit in hutches like this one, they eat carrots and lettuce, and, oh yes, human children think they're wonderful."

"Well they must do more than that, surely," Tushtots demanded.

"Well they've got nice soft fur, I suppose. Take a closer look, Willi," ordered Ginger. Willi Whizkas crept closer towards the rabbit, who promptly turned on his big floppy feet and disappeared into the hole in the side of the hutch.

"Well he's a funny timid little thing," observed Tushtots "hasn't got much of a tail has he, and did you see those ears? He'll be able to hear the dawn break with those!" All three cats sat down and waited for the rabbit to come back out again, watching a twitching nose and a set of whiskers looking back at them from the gloomy inside of the hutch.

"Please don't frighten my rabbit," pleaded the little girl, who had come out into the garden without the cats noticing. "His name is Archibald, I'm going to feed him," she pushed a few lettuce leaves and sliced carrots through the wire, saying gently to the rabbit "Come on Archi, these cats won't hurt you, they're my friends," as she stroked each cat in turn.

"You wait there," she commanded as she ran off to the house, returning with an older female human who asked "Are these are you new friends?"

"Yes," she replied, "they've been looking after Archibald."

"Well just make sure you don't let Archibald out into the garden when the cats are about."

"Why not?" The little girl enquired.

"Well . . . " her mother struggled for an explanation.

"I wonder," thought Willi Whizkas "I wonder if rabbits taste nice?" The other two were having the same thought as all three cats peered into the cage wondering just how good a rabbit could taste.

16 Thugsby

It was the usual cat meat again for Willi Whizkas, it didn't matter how much he left uneaten, he was still given the same stuff. He licked some of the gravy off and nibbled at a couple of the anonymous lumps. It seemed to lack that certain something that a juicy plump sparrow or a succulent baby starling had, not that he'd had one of those for a long time. "Chance would be a fine thing," thought Willi Whizkas as he was cast out into the garden. He had his usual sniff around, stopping at all the bushes which were likely to have been scent-marked by other cats. He could tell by the smell which cats had been in his garden, Ginger Tompkins had for certain, but there was one strange scent mark which didn't ring a bell at all with him, so he backed up to the bush and flourished his tail. "That will get rid of that," he thought to himself. He wandered over to the pampas grass and gave that a good sniff too, before spraying some more. His female human banged the kitchen window at him, so he stared back vacantly as if to say "Who? Me? What am I doing wrong?" He was still hungry and felt an overwhelming urge to pay Gordon's breakfast plate a visit. On the way he caught sight of the postman with a muzzled Snapper the poodle doing the delivery round. Snapper let out a few muffled barks then began tugging at the lead as he tried to chase Willi Whizkas, but he was soon reeled in by the postman and told off for being a bad dog. True to form Gordon had left quite a lot of his breakfast, so Willi Whizkas began nervously devouring the remains. He wasn't sure what colour tin Gordon's food came from, but it definitely wasn't the green cans! Mission accomplished he shot through the catflap undetected as he thought, but halfway down Gordon's drive he caught sight of a pair of cats eyes glaring at him from under a parked car. Willi Whizkas stopped in his tracks, was this the strange cat who has been scent marking his garden? If so he was going to have it out with him!

"Calm down, calm down Willi," a gruff voice commanded from under the car, "don't you recognise me?"

Willi Whizkas sat in the road and stared. "I'm not sure I do," he said quizzically

"You should do," the stranger replied, "It's thanks to you that I'm the cat I am." Willi Whizkas studied him as he emerged from under the car, he felt there was something familiar about him.

"You're not that skinny little starved wretch Thugsby?"

"I certainly am!" Thugsby confirmed.

"Well you look marvellous now," Willi Whizkas complemented him, "your tummy's filled out, your coat's glossy and you have fabulous whiskers. Surely Gordon doesn't leave that much food?"

"Oh, it's a long story," began Thugsby "but I'll make it as brief as I can. I used to help myself to Gordon's breakfast when he wasn't around, just like you showed me. When his humans went away for a week, a kind lady used to pop round twice a day to feed Gordon, the goldfish and his bird, anyway she caught me red-handed, or should that be red-pawed," he sniggered, "when she saw what a poor specimen I was she adopted me. It took several trips to the vets to put my poorly teeth right, and rid me of fleas and worms. Plus of course there was the little operation that we toms end up having."

"I know the one," Willi Whizkas whispered quietly.

"Still, that's all behind me now, I get as much food as I want in exchange for a few hours sitting on an old lady's knee."

"Well I never!" Willi Whizkas said in astonishment. "Has Ginger Tompkins seen you recently?

" I don't think so," replied Thugsby.

"Well let's go and find him." But no matter where they looked, they couldn't find Ginger Tompkins, so the pair sat on his garden wall and swotted a few bluebottles.

"Do you ever miss your old life Thugs?" Willi Whizkas asked curiously.

"I do sometimes," Thugsby replied with a distant look in his eye, "I don't see my old pals, I miss the adventures we used to get up to, but I'm glad I traded them all in for a cosy place to sleep and a full tummy. I've been thinking about paying my old pals a visit, just for old times sake. Do you fancy coming Willi, it doesn't look like Ginger Tompkins is going to show up."

"OK" agreed Willi Whizkas "why not?" The first stop was the haunted house.

"Let's go inside," invited Thugsby. Willi Whizkas drew in a deep breath then hesitated for a moment.

"Well . . . I'm not too sure," he replied nervously

"It's not really haunted," reassured Thugsby "It's just somewhere old human tramps stayed, they liked people to think the house was haunted, so that other humans would stay away. Sometimes there's a juicy rat to be had in the cellar. I've eaten many a rat down there." Willi Whizkas tried to imagine what a rat tasted like.

"May be next time," he said thinking of all the horrible things rats eat as they scurry around down damp dirty drains.

"Lets go and meet some of my old pals then," Thugsby said, "We'll go through the garden and over to the shops."

Willi Whizkas had never been that far before and didn't even know what a shop was.

"It's where humans go to buy cat meat amongst other things," explained Thugsby. The first shop had a large poster of a cat eating hungrily from a bowl next to the green cat meat tin that Willi Whizkas knew all too well.

"I don't believe that cat is enjoying that for one moment," he muttered to himself. The next shop however looked far more interesting.

""It's a butchers shop," explained Thugsby, "it's where humans buy beef, lamb, chicken, bacon, and even rabbit! Sometimes there's a lady who'll throw you a piece of fat, so if we sit here and look hungry we just might be in luck."

Hang on," mused Willi, "Did you say 'rabbit?'""

"Oh yes, humans eat rabbits all right," confirmed Thugsby.

"Do they?" Willi Whizkas asked in astonishment, thinking about Archibald the rabbit who lived next door to him. If the humans were going to eat Archibald, then Willi Whizkas was going to miss out, so he made up his mind to make the rabbit his number one priority.

"Doesn't look like we're in luck today," Thugsby grumbled as no scraps were forthcoming. "Never mind, there's always the bins round the back." In the alley at the back of the butcher's shop they found a big black tom with his head in a bin trying to drag a huge ham bone out.

"Hey up Perce," yelled Thugsby. Percy Slasher, to give him his correct name, stared back.

"Thugsby. Is that you?" he mumbled around the huge bone in his mouth.

"Yes it is," Confirmed Thugsby.

"My word, whose bin have you been raiding?" Percy Slasher enquired, somewhat jealously.

"I don't raid bins any more, I got rehomed, thanks to this chap here." As Percy Slasher licked and chewed on the bone Thugsby told his tale, but Willi Whizkas had heard it all before so he decided to have a rummage in the bins for himself, sending clouds of bluebottles into the air.

"This would be paradise for Tushtots and Ginger Tompkins, they could hold the 'World Swot the Bluebottle Championship here," he commented.

"Good choice of bin," commented Percy Slasher, "Bluebottles are especially crisp and crunchy at this time of year, and the maggots are exquisitely tender if eaten young."

"Bleeeeurgh" thought Willi Whizkas, he'd rather eat cat meat from the green cans. He realised just how fortunate he was not to have to eat such disgusting food.

"Have you seen any of the old gang?" Thugsby asked Percy Slasher.

"Like who?"

" Rumpuss, Broozer, Badpuss and Grunter?"

"Yes, they're still around, we shared some scraps this morning. I think they've gone off for a cat nap."

"We'll go and look for them," said Thugsby, eager to see his old pals again. The back gardens in this area were very different to those in Willi's road, there were rusty old cars with no windows, and black bags full of rubbish.

"A meal opportunity in my old days," Thugsby told him as they passed overgrown gardens and small children throwing stones.

"Have to be careful here," whispered Thugsby, "the natives aren't too friendly." They picked their way through the grass and tumble-down sheds looking for Thugsby's old pals but they were nowhere to be seen. The gardens came to an end at a very busy road.

"Look at all those cars!" Willi Whizkas exclaimed.

The noise of the engines and the fumes from the exhaust pipes put him off wanting to venture any further. "You don't go across there?" Willi Whizkas asked.

"Only very late at night when most of the cars have gone away, but it's too busy to try now."

There was no sign of Rumpuss, Broozer, Badpuss or Grunter so they turned tail and headed home.

"Never mind," said Thugsby with an air of disappointment in his voice, "after all, it's your future that counts, your past is only where you came from." They were almost back at the butcher's shop when the ugliest mongrel dog the world had ever seen ambushed them. He had venom in his eyes and his snapping jaws meant business. The cats raced behind the bins, knocking a couple over with a clatter as the viscous mongrel crashed towards them. There was nowhere to run, and Willi Whizkas shook with fear, but Thugsby had seen it all before, he knew just what to do. He rose to his full height then sprang out at the dog, claws flailing, hissing and spitting. He sank his teeth into one of the dog's ears, and scratched him across his nose. Willi Whizkas didn't witness the fight, he was too busy cowering behind the bins with his eyes firmly closed. The dog let out a loud yelp of pain and terror then scarpered, while Willi Whizkas emerged nervously from behind the overturned bins and couldn't believe that Thugsby had saved the day.

"I've seen many a dog off in my time," Thugsby told him, "You have to when you're an alley cat."

"I think we should get out while the going's good," pleaded Willi Whizkas wanting to get back to familiar territory, so the cats retraced their steps towards Gordon's house.

"That's where I live now, over there," pointed out Thugsby. "Are you coming to see my new home, Willi?"

"Another time, Thugs, thanks all the same. I think I'll

go home and have a lie down, I've had enough excitement for one day." To which Thugsby replied "That's a shame, I've got a new toy to try out."

"New toy, what's that, a catnip mouse?"

"No, something much better than that," Thugsby informed him "The human handyman came round yesterday and fitted the kitchen door with a brand new catflap."

"Catflap!" Willi Whizkas snapped, "Hmmmppf, the whole world has a catflap except me!" As he was about to cross the road he spotted Gordon sitting on the bonnet of the car that Thugsby had been hiding under that very morning.

"Some rascals had my breakfast again!" Gordon called over to him, and gave Willi Whizkas a very hard stare.

"Well, that's what happens when you have a catflap," replied Willi Whizkas smugly.

17 Archibald the Rabbit

It was early evening when Willi Whizkas finally decided to go home. He'd been out all day looking for things to chase with Ginger Tompkins and Tushtots. They'd played 'swot the bluebottle', 'smack the ant' and 'bat the beetle' amongst the tall flowers in the garden where the human who enjoyed gardening lived. They had found some very strange flies indeed, which looked rather like wasps. Willi Whizkas knew all about wasps, having once been stung on the tongue when he unwisely caught one in his mouth. But these flies could go forwards, backwards, up and down and even remain suspended in the air, which is how the hoverfly got its name. To Willi Whizkas and his pals these flies were just one of nature's curiosities, put there for cats' amusement. They had spent a happy hour or two chasing after the strange flies, crashing through flower beds and flattening vegetables until they were totally exhausted. They then had to spend the rest of the afternoon asleep in the shade of the potato patch. The earth was nice and warm so the cats slept undisturbed until the gardener began to water the garden with a hose pipe. To start with, Willi Whizkas thought it was rain, but once he started to get very wet he decided to dart back to his own garden. This movement attracted the gardener's attention, and, having already noticed the damage that they had caused he turned the hose full on them, shouting angrily at them as the cats ran for their lives.

Willi Whizkas arrived panting at the bottom of his own garden to discover his humans sitting in deck chairs with the people from next door.

"Here he is," announced Willi's female human, "Come on you old flea-bag, come and meet your new neighbours," but of course Willi Whizkas already knew his new neighbours, especially the little girl. It made perfect sense to Willi that if he was going to get a closer look at the lop-eared rabbit, then his best plan was to make friends with the little girl, which is exactly what he did. The little girl ran excitedly across the lawn, picked him up around his tummy and marched him triumphantly to the adults.

"Don't squeeze him too tight," her mother warned.

"No, You'll make him sick," added the other parent, so she put him down and gave him a good stroke instead. Willi Whizkas started to fuss around her legs, his tail went up her skirt and tickled her knees, which made her squeal with laughter.

"Look at Willi Whizkas, look at Willi Whizkas," she called, and everybody laughed as Willi Whizkas rolled over onto his back, put his legs in the air inviting the little girl to stroke his tummy. Cats will often take advantage of a situation like this to give humans a good scratching, but he resisted the temptation, as thoughts of the rabbit were foremost in his mind. Having made a good impression with everybody he decided to put one of his back legs into the air and polish his bottom just as the humans were about to dig into a large pile of sandwiches.

"Oi, Willi you vile creature, can't you leave that bottom of yours alone for five minutes? I think you'd rather lick your bottom than eat your cat food," wailed his female human as she hurled a flip flop at him. Willi Whizkas sprang up in surprise then ran indoors, but it was a nice warm evening, so he decide not to not stay in for the night, and went back out almost immediately. All night, whenever he wasn't prowling around listening to hedgehogs crunching snails he was thinking about Archibald, the rabbit next door. At one point he actually went into next door's garden and crept silently up to the rabbit hutch. He wasn't expecting to come face to face with the Archibald, he was expecting him to be tucked away on his bed of straw, but as it was a warm evening Archibald was sitting at the wire mesh with his nose twitching and his whiskers quivering. He didn't see Willi Whizkas creeping up on him, and Willi Whizkas didn't see the rabbit until they were almost nose to nose. Willi Whizkas was just about to poke a paw through the wire when Archibald came to his senses, spun round and in an instant gave the wire, and Willi's nose, an almighty kick with his huge back paws. Willi Whizkas reeled back quite shocked and dazed as Archibald hopped through the hole into his bedchamber.

Willi Whizkas wasn't sure what to make of rabbits now, he had been expecting an easy meal, but Archibald could look after himself, that was obvious. Archibald had caught him with one of his claws, the chastened tom could taste blood.

"Oh no," thought Willi Whizkas, if it was a bad cut then it would almost certainly mean a trip to the vet, So he decided to make himself scarce. The next morning his female human soon tired of calling him so she left his food outside the kitchen door, locking it behind her. Willi Whizkas was more concerned about his nose than his breakfast, so he thought he would visit Tushtots and get a second opinion. It was painful to push Tushtots's catflap open with his scabby nose, Tushtots' mouth dropped open as he saw the battered face poking through his catflap.

"My goodness Will's, what has happened to you? Just look at that nose, who have you been picking a fight with?

"The truth is stranger than fiction," Willi Whizkas told him as his sorry tale began. He told Tushtots all about his encounter with Archibald the lop-eared rabbit. while Tushtots listened with interest.

"That's a nasty looking nose though," he told Willi Whizkas.

"Does it look like a visit to the vets?" Willi Whizkas asked anxiously.

"It's touch and go," Tushtots replied, "if you don't want to go, you'd better lie low for a few days and hope it gets better, but if it gets infected you'll wish you had gone, especially if your nose drops off!"

Willi Whizkas felt even more downhearted at the prospect of his nose taking a turn for the worse but he couldn't stop himself from licking it, soon his raspy tongue knocked the scabs off so it started to bleed again. He did his best to keep out of his humans' way but it was no good, his nose had now started to swell and weep pus. He went to see Ginger Tompkins to get his opinion and had to tell his sorry tale all over again.

"Looks like the vets to me, old chap," Ginger Tompkins commented, so Willi Whizkas reluctantly went home to face the music and to wait for the inevitable. He didn't have to wait long for his two humans to manhandle him into his basket. He wouldn't have minded if he had been fighting, rather than simply succumbing to a rabbit punch!

Willi Whizkas mewed pitifully all the way to the vets. The worst bit wasn't actually seeing the vet, it was the endless time spent in the waiting room with all manner of dogs, cats, and things unseen in cardboard boxes tied up with string with little air holes punched in. Frightened cats would let out plaintive mews, but none were as loud as Willi's. There was always an inquisitive dog who's owners would let it loose in the waiting room to visit each patient in turn. Willi Whizkas darted a paw out at the dark crusty nose as it came towards him, letting out a warning hiss.

"Come back here Ghengis," the dog owner snapped and thankfully the dog was once again attached to his lead. Willi Whizkas was almost last to go in, but finally he was placed unceremoniously onto an examination table still damp with disinfectant from the last patient.

"Now then, what seems to be the matter?" Enquired the vet, but he didn't require an answer once he caught sight of Willi's glowing nose.

"Let's clean that up a bit for you old lad," said the vet, pressing an antiseptic swab onto Willi's nose. His head felt like it was going to explode when the stinging solution was dabbed firmly onto his poor inflamed nose, he squirmed and growled, but to no avail. An antibiotic injection was then jabbed firmly into his neck. His humans were given a packet of pills to take away before he was bundled back into his basket with a sore neck as well as a sore nose. His humans whinged on about the costs all the way home, they told him he had to stay inside for at least two days until the swelling on his nose went down and he could breathe properly. An old blanket was put on his favourite spot on the work surface and he was bedded down for the night with a reassuring stroke.

"You'll feel better in a day or so," he was told as he drifted off to sleep feeling a little better already. The following morning he jumped down off the blanket eager to see what was on offer for breakfast. Keeping out of his humans' way for the past few days so that they wouldn't see his nose meant that he'd missed out on a couple of meals along the way. But there was something different about the usual gunge from the green can, it didn't smell right for one thing, and someone seemed to have stirred it, but hunger got the better of him. He was about half way through when something really nasty hit his taste buds, he spat it out and there it was, a small pink pill!

"Now come on you bad cat," one of his humans scolded, "it's for your own good. If you don't eat it, I shall have to make you swallow it." Willi Whizkas stood by the back door and yowled to be let out, if he'd had a catflap he would have been off! Instead he was scooped up and plonked onto the draining board where a kitchen towel was wound around him restraining his paws and claws, so that only his head was visible. He was tipped onto his back, his mouth was prized open then the pink pill was plopped into his mouth. He promptly spat it out.

"You need to gently tap him on his throat," his male human advised. Again the pill was pushed into his mouth, his throat was gently tapped, before he knew it the pill had gone.

"There we are," said his human as he was released from the towel, but he still wasn't allowed out into the garden. The humans went to work and left him shut in the kitchen with his litter tray. Tushtots came into the garden looking for him around lunchtime, but all Willi Whizkas could do was stare at him from the kitchen windowsill. Tushtots wasn't expecting Willi Whizkas to be shut in the house, it was some time before he caught sight of him. Tushtots gave an athletic leap and attempted to get a pawhold on the windowsill, but the plastic was too slippery so he fell off, landing on all four paws in true cat style. Willi Whizkas chuckled to himself as Tushtots tried again, but it was no use, the ledge was too slippery and narrow. So Tushtots jumped onto the wheelie bin instead, it was difficult for Tushtots to hear what Willi Whizkas was saying, but he did manage to make out "Vets" . . . "Injection" . . . "Pills" and "kept in."

There was no way Tushtots could get in and there was no way Willi Whizkas could get out. If he had gone to the vets straight away he would be well on the road to recovery and able to have adventures with Tushtots and Ginger Tompkins. As for Archibald, that was still unfinished business!

18 The Photograph

Willi's nose was gradually getting better. The tablets that he was forced to take twice a day had worked, he could now breathe properly and smell things, especially where other cats had scent marked his bushes. He was checking the bushes when he heard the little girl from next door, whispering,

"Puss, puss puss, come here Willi Whizkas." He liked the little girl and he had liked the thought of rabbit until the incident with his nose, but now he wasn't too sure what to think about Archibald. If getting close to that rabbit meant paying another visit to the vets, then perhaps he ought to keep away. But the little girl kept pestering him, she finally persuaded him to squeeze into her garden. She was sitting cross-legged holding a tempting piece of chicken skin high in the air. Willi's tail stood erect, he let out a little mew and began to purr softly as his eyes followed the chicken skin up and down. Finally he leapt up, snatched it, gulped and it was gone. The little girl laughed and stroked him as he licked his lips and looked for more, letting out a pleading miaow. "Sorry, there's no more," she said apologetically.

Willi Whizkas had nothing planned for the morning so he was quite happy to sit on the grass with her in the sunshine. The little girl ran into the house then came back with a length of string with an old pigeon feather tied to the end. She started to tease Willi Whizkas with the feather, before long he was chasing the little girl, the string and the feather round and round the lawn. Both

Willi Whizkas and the little girl enjoyed the game, but Willi Whizkas eventually ran out of puff and had to lie down for a rest.

"You poor tired little kitten," she told him, "I have just the thing for you," she disappeared into the garage, coming back a few moments later wheeling an old pink dolls pram which had been her grandmothers. It had been handed down to the little girl to play with, and she used it for all sorts of things, like pushing it to the shops with her mother filled with fruit and flowers. Any old ladies that they passed along the way expected to see a baby doll inside, but she didn't have a doll which would fit in the pram, until today. Judging Willi Whizkas to be the ideal size, she pulled the hood back, lifted the cover then took out a small fleecy blanket no bigger than a hand towel and proceeded to wrap Willi Whizkas inside it. It was a bit of a struggle lifting Willi Whizkas up as he was quite a heavy cat, and she was only a small girl, but after a bit of effort Willi Whizkas found himself lying in the pram on his back being tucked in with a frilly pink bonnet tied round his head. The little girl laughed out loud, and pushed the pram over to the kitchen window. Her mother was washing up after breakfast, looked down to see what her daughter was up to. She couldn't quite make out what was going on, so she went outside to find out.

"What a big soft cat you are William," the mother laughed, as she tickled him under his chin. If he could have seen how ridiculous he looked he would have jumped out a long time ago, but he was warm, comfortable and getting plenty of attention so he was happy to stay were he was, despite being the source of some mild amusement. The little girl's mother went into the house and returned a minute or so later with, of all things, her camera.

"Smile, you big daft cat," she laughed, then a blinding flash stunned Willi Whizkas for a second or two, while the mother turned and returned back into the house, still chuckling.

"There," said the little girl to Willi Whizkas, "you've had your photograph taken," which meant about as much to Willi Whizkas as algebra does to a toad. The hood was then pulled up on the pram, Willi Whizkas was slowly pushed up and down the garden path while the little girl sang to him.

All this time they were being watched by two pairs of inquisitive eyes, who couldn't believe what they were seeing. As she turned the pram round and started back towards the house Ginger Tompkins and Tushtots could see what the little girl had in her pram, they peered down from the fence at Willi's face, framed by the ridiculous pink bonnet. Ginger Tompkins and Tushtots looked at each other in disbelief, then back at Willi Whizkas soundly asleep, unaware that he was being observed by his closest friends, who decided for the moment to stay quiet and not wake him from his slumber. He stayed in the pram for most of the morning, his reward for being a good 'baby' and playing so nicely with the little girl was more chicken skin plus a few scraps she'd picked from the bones.

The little girl had to go out shopping with her mother for the afternoon so Willi Whizkas was given a final stroke and the little girl kissed him on the top of his head. As he started to wander off back home he couldn't resist having a sly look at the rabbit who was sitting in his cage munching dandelion leaves.

"Yes my lad," thought Willi Whizkas to himself, "wait till I catch you outside that cage."

He jumped over the fence into Tushtots' garden where he found Tushtots and Ginger Tompkins sitting on the patio patting a large black beetle and seeing off some troublesome ants.

"Hello," Tushtots greeted him, "what have you been up to this morning?"

"Oh, just … you know . . . bit of this, bit of that, nothing in particular," replied Willi Whizkas in an unconvincing manner as he examined a claw rather closely, trying not to look directly at Tushtots and Ginger Tompkins.

"Oh, right," said Tushtots, "you haven't been in the little girls garden, then?"

"Well, I might have popped over," Willi Whizkas fibbed, "just to have a look at the rabbit, you know."

"Well you're here now old chap," smirked Ginger Tompkins "what shall we do this afternoon?"

"Sleep." Willi Whizkas yawned, quite exhausted by the mornings inactivity.

A couple of days later Willi Whizkas saw the little girl in her garden again, remembering how well he had been looked after before, he decided to pay her a visit. The little girl was delighted to see him, picking him up for a kiss and cuddle.

"There you are Willi Whizkas, I've got something special for you!" She set him down on the patio table, gave him a little stroke and instructed him to "stay there." She then ran to the kitchen and came back carrying a small box of cat biscuits, which he eyed with anticipation. The little girl struggled to open the box as Willi Whizkas shamelessly nuzzled her, then when the biscuits burst clumsily from the box he greedily gulped them down, crunching the big ones while swallowing the small ones whole.

"Not too many now," called the little girl's mother, "otherwise he won't eat his tea when he goes home." But it was too late, he had managed to gobble down most of them. He stretched his neck, let out a couple small burps to the delight of the little girl, then started to lick his lips and wash his whiskers.

"I think it's time for your sleep now," the little girl told him and went to fetch the little blanket that he had been wrapped up in before. She carried him over to the doll's pram and popped him in, tying this ears up in the little pink bonnet. But today it was a bit of a squeeze, in fact there was very little room for him, as he turned his head, he could see why. Sticking out from under a small blue bonnet were two huge ears! Archibald the rabbit was fast asleep, totally unaware that Willi Whizkas was being tucked up next to him. Willi was wrapped too tightly in his blanket to do anything about it, so Willi Whizkas and Archibald were now the little girl's twins for the afternoon.

The pram was pushed up and down the road as she sang little songs that she made up about Willi Whizkas and Archibald and how much she loved them. Willi Whizkas had quite enjoyed it when it had been just him in the pram, but having to share with a big fat viscous rabbit, who was now wide awake and glaring murderously at him was a different matter altogether!

Unknown to Willi Whizkas he was being watched by a disbelieving Gordon from the bedroom window of his house. Tushtots and Ginger Tompkins had told him all about Willi Whizkas and the doll's pram, now he was seeing for himself. However he hadn't a clue what the creature with the enormous ears was. It certainly wasn't like anything Gordon had seen at home, in the garden or in the allotments. He watched as the little girl decided to see just how fast she could push the doll's pram, she began to race up and down the drive, faster and faster until the wheels on one side of the pram left the path, sank into a flower bed then tipped the pram and its contents over. The little girl squealed as the pram crashed onto its side spilling Willi Whizkas and Archibald the rabbit onto a lavender bush. Willi Whizkas untangled himself from the blanket and, thinking it was his chance to get his own back on Archibald, he pounced on the rabbit and tried to sink his teeth into one of Archibald's ridiculously large ears. But Archibald was having none of it, he sprang to his feet, throwing Willi sideways as he did so. He then charged in Willi's direction, showing two huge front teeth. Not wanting another trip to the vets Willi Whizkas dashed across the lawn, squeezed through the hedge into his own garden and made good his escape. Tushtots and Ginger Tompkins were waiting for him, they had seen the whole episode unfold and just laughed and laughed at Willi Whizkas, who still had his pink bonnet on with a little hint of lipstick on his nose where the little girl had kissed him.

"Well, Willi you big girl!" Ginger Tompkins sniggered, "there's no fibbing your way out of this one, how was it sharing a pram with that rabbit who, you told us, was going to be your dinner? You soon scarpered when he showed you his teeth," they fell about laughing again. Willi Whizkas was very embarrassed, he didn't know what to say, but rather than stay and be teased he made an excuse that he had to go inside. However his embarrassment was far from over, as that evening when his humans came home, the little girl's mother knocked on their door and presented them with a large colour photograph of their beloved Willi Whizkas wearing a pink bonnet, tucked up in the doll's pram.

"Willi Whizkas," laughed his female human "is there something you need to tell us?" He took one look at the picture and fled.

19 Mewkus

All the troubles in the world usually find their way to Willi's door, but today it was Tushtots' turn. Over the past few months all had been well, he had a lovely new home, caring humans, all the food he could wish for and two of the best friends a cat could hope to make in Ginger Tompkins and Willi Whizkas. Life had never been so sweet, even his fur which had been shaved off was nearly grown back again. But a phone call the previous evening to Tushtots' humans was about to change everything. It was the lady from the animal charity which had found Tushtots his new home ringing up to see if his humans could take in another cat, just for a week while the sanctuary shut down for a holiday. His humans agreed, so in due course a small white van arrived, a yowling hissing sneezing moggy was brought to the door in a reinforced cat basket. Tushtots' eyes were as big as saucers and as black as coal when he surveyed the growling, sneezing monster that lurked behind the bars.

"What on earth is that?" Tushtots thought to himself as he felt a twinge of insecurity.

"Keep him in for a couple of days," instructed the van driver, "then he should be OK to go outside for the rest of the week. His name is Mewkus, when he comes out you'll see why." The cage was tipped up and Mewkus plopped out onto the carpet with more hissing, growling and sneezing. Tushtots shrank back towards the kitchen door as Mewkus jumped onto the windowsill, knocked over a flower vase and began pawing at the window pane, his hissing and growling only interrupted by violent sneezing.

"Right. I'll leave him with you," smirked the van driver as he beat a hasty retreat. Mewkus hid behind the sofa as the flowers were put back into the vase and the water was mopped up, while Tushtots shot across the kitchen and out through his catflap thinking the garden was the safer place to be.

Willi Whizkas was on his way over to see if Tushtots was up for an adventure.

"Not today Willi Whizkas, something terrible has happened."

"Calm down, calm down," instructed Willi Whizkas, "what do you mean something terrible has happened?"

"I think I'm being replaced," cried Tushtots."

"Being replaced Tushtots, what nonsense!" Willi Whizkas laughed.

"It's true," insisted Tushtots, "this awful cat called Mewkus was delivered to my house this morning, just like I did. In fact I think he has come in the same basket that I did."

While Tushtots told Willi Whizkas the story of the morning's events, the house was being organised for Mewkus' stay. An extra litter tray was put down, a second feeding bowl and most importantly, the catflap was locked until Mewkus was familiar with his temporary home.

"A new arrival then," commented Willi Whizkas after Tushtots had finished his tale "we'd best go and have a look at the newcomer, give him the once over."

"I don't really want to go," moaned Tushtots miserably," he's done nothing but growl, sneeze and knock things over."

"I'll judge for myself, he might be a decent sort once we get to know him."

"Yes, but what about me," wailed Tushtots, "what if he has come to replace me and I have to go back to the sanctuary?"

"Nonsense, you've been a model cat," assured Willi Whizkas as he tried to push Tushtots' catflap open.

"Ooops, that's odd," commented Willi Whizkas as he pushed again, "it seems to be jammed."

"What!!" Tushtots exclaimed, "they've locked me out, I told you something like this would happen." He pushed Willi Whizkas aside then shoved the catflap for all he was worth, but it wouldn't budge. Tushtots' mood sank into depression, then he let out a deep sigh.

"Should have known life was too good to be true," he mumbled. Willi Whizkas tried to cheer him up, he suggested that they look through a window into the house, so they jumped onto the windowsill and tried to peer in, though the net curtains made it difficult.

"Can't see him," said Willi Whizkas.

"He's in there all right," growled Tushtots, then they heard a loud voice bellow from inside the house.

"Get down, you naughty cat!" It was one of the humans yelling at Mewkus, who was trying to climb the curtains, pulling out big threads as he went up.

"Well I don't think you have much to worry about," comforted Willi Whizkas, "he won't last long." Tushtots hung around the garden all morning, every now and then he would try the catflap, but it was still locked. As the afternoon wore on no amount of comforting from Willi Whizkas or Ginger Tompkins, who had now joined them, was going to make Tushtots feel any better. It was now time for Willi's and Ginger Tompkins' humans to come home from work, which meant food, so they left Tushtots all alone pondering his fate. Eventually Tushtots' humans opened the kitchen door and shouted.

"Tushtots, puss puss, come on, tea time." Tushtots was so relieved to hear his name that he ran up to the house, but was stopped in his tracks by a particular scent. A scent which told him that another cat had used his litter tray!

"Come on Tushtots," encouraged his humans, "come in if you want your tea," one nervous paw followed the other until he was just far enough in for the door to be shut behind him.

"Come on Tushtots, tuna tonight," but he had barely made a start on the juicy chunks when Mewkus ran into the kitchen, shoved Tushtots away from the tuna, hissed, curled his tongue, showed his fangs and sneezed snottily.

"No need for that," instructed a human "you've had more than enough food today my lad, that's Tushtots' tuna, let him finish in peace." Mewkus was shooed back into the lounge, the door shut behind him to give Tushtots a bit of breathing space. That evening Tushtots clamped himself firmly onto his human's lap and purred whilst keeping one eye on the new arrival, but Mewkus couldn't settle down so wandered round sniffing at things. Suddenly a loud crash was heard from the dining room, Tushtots was suddenly ejected from his human's knee as he sprang up to go and investigate. Mewkus had jumped onto the table, sending a bowl of fruit crashing to the floor.

"Oh dear, oh dear, what are we going to do with you, Mewkus? I think we'd better shut you in the kitchen for your own safety."

Later that evening Mewkus and Tushtots were dumped in the kitchen and the door was firmly closed behind them.

The first thing that Mewkus did was to jump onto the work surface and sniff around a shrink-wrapped chicken that had just been taken out of the freezer. He licked the moisture off the outside of the plastic and tried tearing at the plastic wrapping, but it was too tough for Mewkus to rip. His attention then turned to a roll of kitchen paper which he knocked over and watched unwind as it rolled across the kitchen floor.

"Oh dear, oh dear," thought Tushtots to himself, "there's going to be trouble before the night is out, I hope I'm not going to get any of the blame." But Mewkus hadn't finished yet, he pawed open the washing machine, climbed in and piddled all over some dirty towels that were waiting to be washed. Tushtots couldn't bear to see any more!

Mewkus seemed to settle down after this naughty little episode, the pair of them curled up for a snooze at opposite ends of the kitchen. It was just getting light when Tushtots was awoken by the sound of cat litter hurtling in all directions across the kitchen. Mewkus had done the smelliest cat poo in the world! Tushtots tried to ignore him, but then Mewkus jumped onto the work surface and returned to the defrosting chicken, which was now softening up nicely. Mewkus began to claw and bite at the wrapper and this time he succeeded in tearing it open. Predictably, the chicken slipped off the work surface and landed with a dull thud on the kitchen floor, taking Mewkus by surprise. Tushtots could only look on in horror and hope the humans wouldn't notice the mess until after he had escaped into the garden. Bored with the chicken Mewkus noticed a cupboard door was open, so he crept inside, soon cups saucers and plates started to rattle as the naughty cat explored, but he soon got bored and came out of the cupboard looking for more mischief. Now came the 'piece de resistance', as Mewkus proceeded to wee all over the top of the cooker, following which he let out a few loud sneezes which brought on a coughing fit, followed by the sound that all cat owners dread the most.

"Bleergh, bleergh, bleergh," the sound of a cat that is about to be sick! Mewkus didn't disappoint. A huge fur ball accompanied by pieces of raw chicken skin was ejected noisily onto the kitchen work surface, a nasty yellow liquid began to trickle over the edge and down the front of the fridge door. Mewkus barely had time to clear his throat when Tushtots heard the familiar sound of his human's alarm clock buzzing.

"We're for it now," Tushtots thought glumly as loud footsteps thundered down the stairs, followed by a loud voice roaring "Phew! What's that smell? – what a stink" as the kitchen door was flung open. The first footstep landed on top of the now fully defrosted chicken, the human slipped and fell on the floor, his hand coming to rest in the used litter tray. As a loud "Arrrrgh" pierced the air, Tushtots made his escape past the flailing human and out through the living room window. He ran and ran until he reached the wall at the bottom of Ginger Tompkins' garden, where he sat down to catch his breath.

"What a night," he puffed, "If I get the blame for any of that I'm definitely on my way back to the cat's home." He thought about staying out for the next couple of days, at least that would prove that he wasn't the cat responsible for the antisocial behaviour. He was relieved to see Willi Whizkas, who happened to be padding around aimlessly.

"What's the matter, Tusher? You're not usually out this early."

"Wait till you hear what sort of a night I've had. I'll tell you all about it if you have a spare hour to two." Tushtots began his sorry tale about Mewkus the naughty cat, but with every event Willi Whizkas began to laugh a little more, by the time Tushtots was reaching the end of his story Willi Whizkas was rolling around on the floor.

"What are we going to do with him?" Tushtots asked when Willi Whizkas finally came to his senses. "I daren't go back home as I'm sure to get the blame."

"I don't think so," Willi Whizkas reassured him, "unless of course you also do naughty things."

"No I don't, the worst I've ever done is use the litter tray, that's only when the catflap was locked and I couldn't get out into the garden."

"Well I think you're in the clear. What you need is a master plan to get rid of Mewkus, one thing's for sure, we can't let him stay and spoil things for you Tusher."

The cats sat in the early morning sunshine while Willi Whizkas tried to come up with one of his moggy-masterplans, but no matter how hard he thought, nothing came to mind.

"Well, we'll never scare him away, "said Tushtots. "He's a real bruiser, always sneezing, I'm sure he's going to give us all cat flu before much longer."

"I think he needs a trip to the vets," Willi Whizkas snorted spitefully.

" I'm starving," grumbled Tushtots "I've not had any breakfast what with this miserable start to the morning. I think we should mooch over to Gordon's for the leftovers."

"You must be desperate Tushtots," Willi Whizkas sympathised, "but I think you'll be better off going to face the music. I'll come with you, if you like." (Willi Whizkas was hoping for an invite to some tasty fare at Tushtots' house.) As the two cats approached Tushtots' kitchen door, it was thrown open and the last of the damage, the chewed chicken, was consigned to the dustbin.

"There you are Tushtots," smiled his human "don't you want your breakfast? Oh, I see you've brought a guest, well come in lads, A hearty breakfast is not to be sneezed at!"

"Unless of course your name is Mewkus," Willi Whizkas whispered to Tushtots as they heard the sound of sneezing coming from the next room.

20 Ginger Tompkins Smells a Rat

After a few days things calmed down in Tushtots's house, the catflap was unlocked and Mewkus began to explore the garden. Tushtots was beginning to like Mewkus a little; after all, he had come from a sad life very much like his own. Meanwhile Mewkus soon became bored, he was looking for a little more excitement, so he pressed Tushtots to show him what passed for fun in these parts. "Well," Tushtots told him, "there's swat the bluebottle."

"Swat the bluebottle?" Mewkus replied sneeringly, "I grew out of that one yonks ago, what about birds, mice and rats? Something to spring out on and chew perhaps?"

"We don't get many birds round here," Tushtots told him, "there are too many cats about."

"Well, there must be mice, every garden has at least one mouse under the garden shed." Tushtots thought about Willi's mouse and how it had been mouse-napped, but decided he'd better not mention it.

"I'll see what I can do," he told Mewkus. "I'll have a word with my mates and we'll see if we can rustle up an adventure for you."

Tushtots told Willi Whizkas of his plight when he saw him later that morning.

"Wants rats and mice does he?" Willi Whizkas pondered, "well there's only one place where there's lots of rats to be had."

"Oh no, you don't mean . . .?" whispered Tushtots fearfully.

"Yes I do, the haunted house. But I don't really like going there myself."

"Nor me," agreed Tushtots, "but we could just take him there and leave him to it."

"Who knows, it may be the rats dining on a cat, now that would be a twist in the tail," chuckled Willi Whizkas.

"Great idea," agreed Tushtots, "perhaps that's how we're going to get rid of him, but just think of it Willi, being eaten alive by rats!"

Both cats thought for a moment and felt a shudder down their spine right to the tips of their tails.

"Be even more scary at night," muttered Willi Whizkas "We'll just take him over to the allotments, show him where to go, then come back when he disappears from view." So that was how Willi's master plan was hatched.

"You go and tell him then," ordered Willi Whizkas, "we'll meet up tonight as soon as it gets dark, as long as I don't get shut in."

"Well all you have to do Wills, is to start gagging like you're going to bring a fur ball up and you'll be out on the lawn before you know it," Tushtots instructed.

"That's true," agreed Willi Whizkas, "good thinking." He sat in the kitchen window after his evening meal, as soon as it got dark he went to the kitchen door and started miaowing, which usually did the trick.

"Shut up you noisy cat," his female human told him, "you've not been in five minutes." Mewing was obviously not going to work. Nothing for it then, it had to be time for 'bring up the fur ball'. For this to be really effective he would need to be sitting on the dining room table, so he jumped up and when he was sure that he had his human's attention he stretched his neck, stuck out his tongue and "Bleergh, bleergh, bleergh," but he wasn't very convincing.

"It's a good brushing you need Willi Whizkas, that will stop you choking." So he was picked up in an ungainly manner and set about with a stiff brush. Twenty minutes later and feeling like he'd lost half his fur he decided only the most drastic action imaginable could achieve his goal, he silently released a rude smell like only cats can, the sort of odour that clings to the air and no amount of wafting will clear.

"Phew, Willi you stinker! You need to go out and freshen up!"

Once Willi Whizkas was out he darted into Tushtots' garden and found Tushtots and Mewkus waiting.

"About time Willi Whizkas, we've been waiting ages for you," Tushtots grumbled.

"Sorry," apologised Willi Whizkas, "the humans wouldn't take the hint so I had to resort to the rude smell trick." With that the three cats trotted over the gardens towards the allotments.

"So where exactly are we going?" Mewkus enquired, but the other two cats wouldn't say.

"You'll see when you get there," Tushtots informed him, "but if it's a bit of sport you're after you won't be disappointed." Mewkus began sniffing under sheds and nosing the compost heaps sneezing as he went.

"You could never lose him with all that noise," Willi Whizkas commented to Tushtots.

"Over this way Mewkus," beckoned Willi Whizkas, "you're wasting your time over there, if it's big game you're after it's over here." They crawled through the overgrown gardens of the haunted house.

"Wow!! This looked exciting," shouted Mewkus, "does anyone live here?"

"No," Willi Whizkas informed him, "unless of course you believe in ghosts."

"No such thing," scoffed Mewkus.

The three cats went into the house through a broken door. Willi Whizkas and Tushtots felt a little uneasy, but there was no stopping Mewkus and he wandered off sniffing and sneezing.

"If you go through that door there," Willi Whizkas suggested, "you go down into the cellar and unless I'm very much mistaken there will be plenty of rats there to keep you amused." Mewkus shot off into the darkness.

"Idiot cat," muttered Tushtots as they turned tail and ran.

"That place really gives me the creeps," shuddered Willi Whizkas when they were back in Tushtots' kitchen.

"Me too," agreed Tushtots through a mouthful of prawns. "Let's hope that's the last we see of him. If the rats don't get him perhaps he'll lose his way back in the dark." The two cats went into the lounge when they had finished eating then began to have a jolly good wash. Tushtots' human beckoned Tushtots to sit on his knee and Willi Whizkas curled up on the sofa, both cats appreciating the post-Mewkus peace and quiet. Just before bedtime the human went into the kitchen to make a cup of cocoa, which grabbed Tushtots' attention as he sometimes got to drink some from a saucer, but at that very moment his ears pricked up and his head span round as he heard a noise at the catflap. He looked at Willi Whizkas and whispered,

"I think Mewkus is back, I thought you said the rats would eat him?" The cats went over to the kitchen door just in time to see Mewkus coming in backwards!!!

"Stupid cat," laughed Willi Whizkas, "I thought he'd mastered the catflap."

"He has," said Tushtots, as Mewkus's tail, then his back

legs, then his front legs and finally his head appeared, pulling something large and squeaking behind him. The two cats yowled in disbelief, the human dropped his cup of cocoa, but it was too late for anyone to do anything as the monster rat that Mewkus had dragged in escaped from his mouth, ran across the kitchen floor straight between Willi Whizkas and Tushtots then disappeared into the lounge.

"Oh my goodness," shouted the human, "you disgusting cat, what have you done?" Mewkus just sneezed proudly. The three cats and the human made for the lounge as one, the rat would have to be caught as soon as possible. The last thing humans liked was sharing their homes with rodents of any sort, let alone huge rats. Willi Whizkas went one way round the sofa, Tushtots went the other and Mewkus looked behind the curtains, while the human just stood with his mouth open in disbelief.

"Come on lads, find him," he ordered, "let's see you earn your keep." They made a sweep of the lounge but there was no sign of the rat. The human disappeared upstairs and came back a few moments later carrying a large cricket bat.

"Have you caught him yet?" He asked, "obviously not, looks like I'll have to do it myself." The human started to lift curtains, move chairs and peer into corners, bat poised at the ready. He pushed the table away from the wall, 'THWACK' the bat crashed down onto the carpet, but the rat was too quick, all three cats pounced as one, but to no avail. The last they saw of the rat was his long tail slithering out of the door and up the stairs.

"Get him, get him," the human screamed. They raced upstairs and through the only open door into the human's bedroom.

"Come on, you first Mewkus," ordered Tushtots, "you bought the blinking thing home!"

"I know," grinned Mewkus proudly. "I though you'd all be pleased to see it."

"I think not," Willi Whizkas sighed as they followed Mewkus gingerly into the bedroom. The human was close behind, but as he switched the light on the rat vanished under the bed, narrowly avoiding another 'THWACK' from the cricket bat. There was enough room under there for a rat, but not a cat, so the human poked and prodded with the cricket bat. Now a cornered rat is a dangerous rat, Tushtots remembered, so he promptly climbed the curtains out of harms way as 'THWACK' the bat come down unsuccessfully for the third time. Mewkus began chasing the rat round, but wasn't quite quick enough, while Willi Whizkas had fun watching the human with the bat and Mewkus' desperate attempts to catch the rat. By then, the rat, in a final attempt to get away, had cornered Willi Whizkas without him realising until it was too late. Willi Whizkas froze in fear. He hated rats, and could see saliva dripping from the rat's fangs as his beady eyes fixed on Willi's throat. The rat was coiled ready to spring at Willi when suddenly Tushtots dropped like a rock from the curtains, landing cleanly on the rat's back killing him stone dead!!

"Hurray, hurray," proclaimed the human, "my brave little Tushtots has saved the day. You cats stay there on guard while I fetch a box to put it in." Three noses sniffed and twitched as they examined the lifeless body of the rat.

"Well done Tushtots," Willi Whizkas said gratefully.

"A masterstroke," agreed Mewkus, "I didn't think for one minute that you'd gone up the curtains out of cowardice, that was your master plan wasn't it?"

"Errr....yes," stuttered Tushtots winking at Willi Whizkas, as the rat's dead body was placed in a small brown box.

"There, that's the end of that, we can all get a decent nights sleep," the human told the cats. "There'll be an extra treat for you tomorrow, Tushtots."

The following morning Mewkus was gone, as, unbeknown to Tushtots, Mewkus' week at their house was up and the man from the animal sanctuary had collected him. Tushtots assumed it was all to do with the rat as he tucked into a tin of red salmon, his very favourite. He then went into the garden for a wash where he found Willi Whizkas rolling around on his catnip bush.

"There you are Willi, well we certainly had some excitement last night!"

"I never knew you had it in you Tushtots," Willi Whizkas told him admiringly.

"I don't." Tushtots meekly replied. "I really did fall off the curtains, as I landed the rat broke my fall, but at least the rat got rid of Mewkus for us, they came to collect him this morning."

At that moment Ginger Tompkins arrived in the garden, flourished his tail then sprayed extravagantly up a rose bush, before catching sight of Willi Whizkas and Tushtots looking very smug indeed.

"Hello, hello old things, what have you been up to?" Ginger enquired. Tushtots looked at Willi Whizkas, who sniggered and said.

"Have we got a story to tell you Ginge, all about Tushtots, the bravest cat in the world!"

"I don't think so," Ginger Tompkins retorted, knowing Tushtots to be a bit on the timid side. "I think you're having me on with one of Willi's tall tales. If I'm not mistaken, I can smell a rat!"

21 Fairground Attraction

Breakfast was going to plan, with the toaster producing perfect toast and the kettle switching itself off when the water boiled. As a special treat Willi Whizkas got fed from a small foil pouch, which was truly delicious, instead of the usual stuff from the green cans.

"Don't expect it everyday, it's expensive."

Had he understood what his female human said he would have told her that if he ate all the stuff from the pouch, and only half the stuff from the tin, it might make more sense to buy the good stuff, but that's humans for you! Willi Whizkas padded out onto the patio. The sun was out and birds were chirping as Willi washed his whiskers contentedly, but his peace was shattered when Ginger Tompkins's battered face emerged through the hedge, followed by a very dejected looking bloodied cat's body with a limp.

"Goodness me!" Willi Whizkas gasped, "what on earth has happened to you?"

"Oh, don't ask . . . " replied Ginger Tompkins, "but if you do ask . . . I'll tell you."

"Go on then," pleaded Willi Whizkas as he gazed pitifully at Ginger Tompkins, who had a torn ear that had been stitched, a huge scratch on his nose which was beginning to form a nasty scab, a half-closed left eye and a badly bitten paw.

"Where do I start," started Ginger Tompkins, "I was taking a short cut across the football field as usual, and there was a event called a funfair there, lots of caravans, and people assembling rides for the humans amusement. I was just passing a very shiny caravan when two ragamuffin tomcats sprang out, they asked me what my business was. I told them that I was Ginger Tompkins and that I was on my way home, they introduced themselves as Dylan the Villain, a mean looking black cat, and One-Eyed-Jack, he'd lost an eye in a fight, and had one rheumy eye left which glared at me. Well, they didn't buy my story that I was on my way home, they accused me of snooping around the funfair, being up to no good. I insisted that I wasn't, but they were having none of it, so they set about me. It could have been much worse but a man with an earring threw a bucket of water over us, so I scarpered straight home, and got taken down to the vets for repairs. I'll tell you what old fruit, a stitch in the ear doesn't half sting!" Willi Whizkas took a sharp intake of breath as he examined the stitches.

"You stay, while I fetch Tushtots, we'll see if he's ever heard of anything so brutal."

On arrival Tushtots was so shocked at the sight of Ginger Tompkins that all he could say was "Dear oh dear oh dear."

"Well, what are we going to do about it?" Willi Whizkas demanded, "We can't just let ruffians pick on local cats!"

"They should be taught a lesson," insisted Tushtots, which was unusual for him as he was usually a peace-loving cat.

"Well, we shall have to have a plan," announced Willi Whizkas.

"I'm not sure you're the cat for the job,." Ginger Tompkins warned.

"This calls for a cat with special talents," Tushtots urged.

"There's only one cat for this," all three cats said in

unison "Stinker of the Yard!" So they all filed down to the police station where they were greeted by a volley of loud barking from Sergeant Fang, the police station's German Shepherd dog.

"It's OK, he's locked in his kennel," advised Stinker. "Hello, hello, hello, what have we here my lad?" He asked as he looked at Ginger Tompkins' wounds. "This looks like foul play, and no mistake!" Ginger's sorry tale came tumbling out.

"Never in all my days as a police cat have I heard anything so despicable."

"So what's to be done with these ruffians, why don't you just lock them up Stinker?" Willi Whizkas asked.

"Put them in the cells!" Added Tushtots.

"Er . . . , I don't think my authority goes that far," Stinker had to admit, "but I could give them a good talking to."

"I don't think that will work," Ginger Tompkins told him, "they didn't want to listen to me when I tried to explain."

"What we need," added Willi Whizkas, "is Thugsby and a few of his alley cat friends . . . "

"You'll not take the law into your own paws," Stinker told them sternly, "We need to have a plan, use the softly, softly approach. First of all we need to keep these rascals under observation."

"How will we do that without being seen?" Tushtots asked. "If they see us watching them we'll be for it, look what happened to Ginge."

"I have the perfect spot," explained Stinker, "the roof of the police station will give us a bird's eye view."

"But won't we slide off?" Willi Whizkas asked.

"Don't be silly young Willi, the police station has a flat roof." It was a bit of a scramble for the cats, they first had to jump onto Fang's kennel, which started him barking madly, then up the wall of the station yard, onto the police garage and one final leap onto the police station roof. The view was indeed perfect and four pairs of eyes were focused on the fairground.

Keep your ears down," ordered Stinker. "We don't want to give ourselves away! "

By now the fairground rides had been assembled, the first customers were beginning to turn up and people were queuing for candy-floss.

"No sign of them yet?" Willi Whizkas asked.

"I can't see them, they're probably lying low," replied Ginger Tompkins.

"Or waiting to spring out on somebody more likely," worried Tushtots to himself.

The cats watched and waited but after a while they all dozed off. Doing nothing was too much like hard work for them, it wasn't until much later that the loud music from the fairground woke them up. Everything was lit up, the waltzers waltzing, the big wheel turning, and the cakewalk walking. Willi Whizkas had never seen such a pretty sight, as lights of every colour flashed and twinkled, squeals and yells of delighted children rang out as they whirled around on the rides.

"Look, there they are," whispered Ginger Tompkins, pointing an accusing claw at the shiny caravan where he had bumped into them.

"Are you sure that's them?" Stinker enquired, "we don't want any false accusations. Could you pick them out in an identity parade?"

"I think a one-eyed cat would be fairly easy to pick out," snorted Tushtots derisively.

"All right, all right," grunted Stinker, "but we've got to be sure of our facts." So the four cats returned their gaze to the pair of ragamuffins in the fairground below just as the two thugs sprang out at an unsuspecting little girl, Dylan the Villain nipping her ankle. The girl was so shocked she dropped her hot-dog which One-Eyed-Jack promptly grabbed, then disappeared behind the caravan, followed immediately by Dylan the Villain.

"Well I've never seen the like," gasped Stinker, "that child was clearly the victim of an assault and robbery. We are dealing with professionals here." After the hot-dog was polished off, more mischief followed as One-Eyed-Jack lifted his tail and sprayed onto the electrical wires behind the rifle range. Moments later there was a shower of blue and yellow sparks as the lights fizzed, phutted and then went out all over the fairground. People were trapped mid-air on the big wheel, the bumper cars stopped bumping, the music slowed down and stopped. This was just a decoy, however, in the confusion the two feline thieves slipped into the hamburger stand and made off with as much as they could carry.

"We are dealing with ruthless career criminals here," declared Stinker. "We need a master plan!" They had all seen what sort of characters they were dealing with, but what could they do about it?

"We'll all meet at the police station tomorrow, in the meantime go home and think about our next move." Stinker stated with authority. "A short sharp shock will teach these naughty cats a lesson, but we don't want to step outside the law do we boys?" So that evening Willi Whizkas, Ginger Tompkins and Tushtots sat on the wall at the bottom of Ginger Tompkins' garden and pondered.

"We don't really want any more bloodshed." Tushtots said

"I do, I'd like to give them a good bashing," argued Willi Whizkas.

"Me too!" Ginger Tompkins agreed.

"But you heard what Stinker said," Tushtots pointed

out, "we could find ourselves in a lot of trouble if things get messy. The last thing we want is a trip to the vets."

"I've got it!" Willi Whizkas announced with a flash of inspiration, "why don't we round up as many of us as we can, march down to the fairground, and frighten them away?"

"I don't think they're going to be very frightened of us, do you old sausage?" Ginger Tompkins said dismissively, "we're not talking lap-cats or cuddle-kittens here."

" It might work," speculated Tushtots, "if we can get eight or ten of us, and we all arch our backs yowl and spit, that should show them who's boss."

"So, how many can we think of then?" Ginger Tompkins asked.

"Well, there's four of us with Stinker."

"Five with Gordon," added Tushtots.

"And what about that Thugsby character?" Willi Whizkas asked, "he knows lots of alley cats. Do you know, my master plan just might work! Ginger Tompkins and I will go and see Thugsby as soon as possible."

"We'll all meet up tomorrow," Tushtots concluded, "and see if we can raise a pussy-posse." Word soon spread, as Willi Whizkas and Tushtots neared the police station the following morning it was obvious from Sergeant Fang's frantic barking that there were cats in the yard. In fact there were eight, namely Gordon, Ginger Tompkins, Stinker of the Yard, Thugsby and his pals Rumpuss, Broozer, Badpuss and Grunter, so Willi Whizkas and Tushtots made ten. Stinker gathered them for a briefing.

"Now, pay attention lads," he commanded, "we are after two despicable characters known as One-Eyed-Jack and Dylan the Villain. When we find them I don't want any fighting, we'll just surround them, give them a jolly good hissing to, oh, and plenty of yowling. With any luck

144

they will flee the vicinity and vanish from my patch."

Excited chirruping then broke out, Thugsby sharpened his claws on the corner of Sergeant Fang's kennel which only made the dog bark more furiously.

"I've a good mind to spray on that dog," commented Willi Whizkas, "seeing as he's behind bars."

"I wouldn't," instructed Tushtots, "I'm sure he'd remember you."

"Right, off we go then," shouted Stinker, "we'll fan out and whoever spots them first must give a three miaow signal."

They set off for the fairground where, one by one, they squeezed underneath the fence trembling with anticipation. But things were not quite as they expected. Ten pairs of eyes blinked in disbelief. The fairground, its caravans and its troublesome cats had all packed up and gone. The Bank Holiday was over, and so was the pussy-posse's adventure!

"That seems to have put an end to that little matter," stated Stinker. "They must have got wind of what was coming their way," he went on, as he let out a large salami flavoured burp.

"That's a shame," grumbled Ginger Tompkins, "I was looking forward to that pair getting their comeuppance."

"Never mind," added Tushtots, "at least things can get back to normal."

"Right, back to the police station for refreshments." Stinker ordered.

"Well, if it's salami sandwiches," drooled Thugsby. They all polished off the titbits that the police put out for Stinker, after which Willi Whizkas made his way over to Sergeant Fang's kennel

"Willi you're not going to . . . ?" Tushtots asked in a shocked voice.

"Oh yes I am," smiled Willi Whizkas, "Ginger

Tompkins' wish may not have come true, but mine will," with no more ado he backed up to the wire mesh of Sergeant Fang's kennel and sprayed and sprayed and sprayed as the other cats cheered him on. Several days later while Willi Whizkas was dozing in the garden Stinker of the Yard came by on one of his patrols.

"Thought you ought to know Sir, a poster has just gone up in the police station with a picture of a fairground, I think there may be another Bank Holiday coming up!" Willi Whizkas just groaned.

22 Dead Sparrows Don't Squawk

Willi Whizkas lazily stepped into his litter tray and made himself comfortable. "Oh no you don't you disgusting cat," his female human shouted, "you can jolly well go in the garden and do that!"

As he dug a hole in the garden he wondered why the litter tray was put there for his convenience, but he wasn't allowed to use it. Having covered over the hole to his satisfaction, it didn't look as though he was going to be let back in for breakfast just yet, so he'd just have to wash his bottom and bide his time. He recognised the little girl's laughter coming from the garden next door, so as breakfast was obviously going to be a long time coming, he went in search of a snack. Poking his whiskers through the hedge, he could see the little girl was examining something very closely and prodding it with a stick, so he went to investigate.

"Oh, there you are Willi," she said to him as he fussed around her legs. "I've not seen you for a while, come and see what I've found!" To his absolute amazement she was looking at a dead sparrow. He pushed forward to give it a sniff, it wasn't every day that he got this close to one of the garden birds.

"My mummy says it could be a baby sparrow that's fallen out of a nest, what do you think Willi?" She asked, bending down to give him a stroke. "You wait there and I'll go and fetch you something to eat from the kitchen."

Willi Whizkas wasn't waiting for anybody, he took the dead sparrow firmly between his teeth and darted back to his own garden. Now, there wasn't much meat on a baby sparrow, but he enjoyed every morsel as he reduced the poor mite to a few feathers and a head. Which left the question of what to with the head. He never really fancied the head, what with the eyes, beak and things, shame to waste it though, so he scooped it up in his mouth and, as many cats do, took it back to show his humans. A few muffled 'miaows' at the door and he was let in, his female human had picked him up for a cuddle and a kiss. 'Bluuurrgh' he let the sparrow's head fall from his mouth, whereupon he was immediately dropped to the floor and given an ear-bashing for killing birds!

"Well, it looks like you've helped yourself to breakfast this morning, you bad cat," he was ejected into the garden once more. A small sparrow wasn't enough to satisfy a growing cat, however, his thoughts turned to Gordon's crusty cat meat dish, so he padded over the road to Gordon's catflap. After he'd polished off the remains of Gordon's breakfast he thought he'd be cheeky and see if Gordon was at home, so he pushed the lounge door open.

"Love you Gordon, Love you Gordon miaow!" Called the bird in the cage, as Willi Whizkas spotted Gordon sitting in the window. Unknown to Willi Whizkas, Gordon had seen him come down the drive.

"Have you finished my cat meat off Willi Whizkas?" Gordon asked.

"Meat? What meat?" Willi Whizkas responded.

"It's the horrible stuff in the green can you know, you always say how much you hate it, but you always come and eat mine," hissed Gordon.

"Perhaps it tastes better when it's dried up?" Willi Whizkas suggested as he jumped up next to Gordon.

"Anything happening out there?" Gordon enquired.

"Nah, not really," replied Willi Whizkas, "oh, I had a sparrow for breakfast this morning, it was dead when I found it, but I still got the blame."

"Dead sparrows can't squawk!" Gordon chuckled at his own joke.

"Ever thought about eating your bird in the cage Gordon?" Willi Whizkas suggested.

"I used to think about it all the time when I was a kitten, I even got on top of the cage once, but the darn thing squawked and squawked till my humans came and told me to leave him alone . . . or else!"

"I expect the feathers would stick in your throat and choke you to death!"

"You're probably right," agreed Gordon.

"What about those great big birds, much bigger than yours Gordon, that the humans buy in plastic bags. There's no feathers and they're really tasty when they've been cooked, the humans give me the leftovers, then they put the bones out in the garden for the birds to peck at." Willi Whizkas told Gordon.

"They're called chickens," Gordon told him condescendingly.

"Well, time to move on," said Willi Whizkas.

"Let yourself out," Gordon told him with a yawn, and Willi Whizkas moseyed on back to his own garden for a much needed snooze. He felt strangely itchy when he woke up, he had to resort to a severe scratch, but the more he scratched, the more he itched, especially round his ears and under his chin. He padded over to Tushtots' house, stopping to scratch several times on the way, and found Tushtots washing his whiskers having eaten a plateful of chicken.

"As soon as I finish my wash I'm going have a sleep," yawned Tushtots

"If you're going on your human's duvet can I join you?" Willi Whizkas asked, stopping for yet another scratch.

"That's a nasty little itch you've got there," observed Tushtots.

"Yes," agreed Willi Whizkas "it started this morning all of a sudden," he went on to describe just how he itched.

"That sounds like fleas to me Wills," Tushtots told him "you've not been near any old hedgehogs have you?"

"No, I haven't seen a hedgehog for ages, but I did pick up a dead sparrow this morning. The little girl next door found it, as I was so hungry I just had to eat it."

"That will be it then," Tushtots told him knowledgeably, "You've picked up a rogue flea or ten. I don't want you on my duvet with fleas. Come to think of it you'd better leave."

"But what can I do?" Willi Whizkas started to panic.

"Well, it's up to your humans to give you treatment, I suggest you start scratching in front of them and they might take the hint."

It was a few days before Willi's humans noticed his condition, and only then by accident. Humans like being bitten by fleas even less than cats do, especially when they're in bed. He had been lying on their duvet, even though it was strictly forbidden, one of his fleas must have jumped off and got into the bed. The next thing he knew he was picked up, turned on his back and his fur searched. This soon confirmed that Willi Whizkas had indeed got a dose of fleas, he heard the word 'bath' mentioned and also 'spray' and 'powder'. He knew what 'spray' meant, this was the air freshener which was liberally sprayed after he had done something smelly in his litter tray, but quite what powder meant he wouldn't find out till the following day. It took both humans to hold him down while the nasty smelly stuff was rubbed into his fur, making his eyes sting and bringing on a sneezing fit. He was sure he had started to foam at the mouth! After this humiliation he was dumped into the garden where he sat scratching and writhing in a cloud of powder. It tasted worse than it smelt, so he couldn't even lick it out of his fur. He wasn't let back into the house that night, despite loud pitiful mewing at the door, so he settled down unhappily under the fir trees. He had a restless night, frequently interrupted by sneezing fits, and when a large hedgehog snuffled by Willi Whizkas let out a loud hiss to send it, and it's collection of fleas, on their way. He did eventually nod off, but not for very long, as the dawn chorus started well before daybreak, it served to remind Willi of birds, sparrows, fleas and powder. It seemed like he couldn't win. Perhaps the cat meat in the green can wasn't such a bad idea after all. The birds in the trees chattered and sang, Willi Whizkas wished he was in the house where it was nice and warm, and quiet! As it became light Ginger Tompkins arrived.

"A little bird tells me you've got fleas," he sniggered, "so I shan't come too close I've had them a couple of times myself old thing, and it's not very nice. Have you had any treatment?"

"I've had the powder," Willi Whizkas informed him with a sneeze.

"Oh, that old fashioned stuff," Ginger Tompkins replied haughtily, "I thought all cats these days had the modern treatment, a couple of drops of liquid on the neck and that's it for months."

"Luxury," muttered Willi Whizkas as he sneezed out another nose-full of powder.

"Never mind, you'll be all right in a couple of days, but I don't think it will kill all those fleas you know," laughed Ginger Tompkins. One by one Willi's itchy patches got less, but word had got round, so every cat kept a safe distance, even the humans wouldn't let him past the lounge door.

Willi dealt with this enforced isolation by spending his time rolling on his cat mint bush, chasing sparrows, and lying in the shade under the car. Not even Tushtots came to see him, and he wasn't welcome in Tushtots' house until his condition had cleared up. A week passed by, Willi's fur was almost back to normal, the fleas had all gone and he felt ready to rejoin feline society, so he went over to see if Tushtots was coming out to play. Willi Whizkas told his pal how he was now fully recovered, the itching had stopped, the smell of the powder had gone away and it was time for an adventure.

"Lets go and see the little girl," suggested Willi Whizkas.

"And why should we want to do that Wills?" Tushtots asked.

"Well," replied Willi Whizkas, "I can think of three good reasons. The first is that she always gives me a nice stroke, secondly she always goes and fetches a nice titbit and thirdly there's Archibald the rabbit. Seeing as how I've gone right off sparrows I've been giving that rabbit quite a bit of thought recently."

"Sounds good to me, let's go."

The little girl wasn't in her garden so they padded up to the patio window and stretched up as far as they could on their back legs, their claws tapping on the glass. The little girl's mother laughed and pointed.

"Look who's come to see you," she said to the little girl, who let out a squeal of delight then raced out into the garden with a box of cat biscuits, which she began to feed one by one to the greedy twosome. The cats loved being hand-fed, and while they crunched their biscuits the little girl gave them both a stroke.

"That'll do, that's enough," instructed the little girl's mummy after five minutes, "they'll be sick if they have too many."

"Right, let's go and have a look at this rabbit," Willi Whizkas commanded as he lead Tushtots to the hutch. The rabbit was sitting by the wire with his nose twitching and his whiskers gleaming in the sunshine, but what particularly amused the cats were those massive ears!!

"Have you ever eaten rabbit Tusher?" Willi Whizkas enquired.

"Not knowingly," came the reply, "but I'm not sure what's in all the scraps I get given."

"Or even what's in the cat meat in the green tin," commented Willi Whizkas.

"Anyway I don't want to put you off or anything, but rabbits get fleas too, in fact there's more on a rabbit than on any sparrow," said Tushtots.

"Fleas, fleas, fleas, That's all I've heard of for the last week," moaned Willi Whizkas, "pesky fleas, let's go to your house Tushtots, and have a sleep on your comfy duvet."

"I'm not sure we'll be allowed," sighed Tushtots miserably, "I was pushed off the duvet last night."

"Fleas?" Willi Whizkas asked smugly.

"No, snoring and rude smells!!!"

23 Willi in the Glasshouse

Willi's morning started with the sound of the kitchen cleaner spray slowly hissing its way along the work surface to where he was curled up over the fridge.

"Come on you lazy cat, shift yourself! Go on, get yourself out into the garden."

He didn't want to go out, it was cold, wet and he was still tired, too much sleep was never enough for a cat. His dreams of chasing mice and birds were often more exciting than having to go out into the real world, especially on grotty days. Instead of going out he nosed the lounge door open and curled up on an easy chair where he was soon fast asleep again. His whiskers and paws were just beginning to twitch, as often happens when a cat is dreaming of chasing a furry breakfast, when the vacuum was switched on. He hated the vacuum, particularly when the human playfully turned the nozzle on him and tried to suck up his tail. He hissed, then shot up the stairs with the tip of his tail twitching in anger, but he soon found himself curled up on the duvet in the spare bedroom ready to pick up his dream where he left off, but that wasn't about to happen.

"You useless cat, get off there, you know you're not allowed in here."

Willi Whizkas slunk into the bathroom and pushed open the towel cupboard where there were nice soft freshly laundered towels just begging to be slept on, but alas! He'd been spotted.

"And don't think you're going in there my lad. You need to go out and freshen up!" With that he was picked up, carried down the stairs then deposited outside the front door.

"That makes a change," Willi Whizkas thought, "I usually get shufted out of the kitchen door, still never mind, I'll go and see Tushtots', I could just do with an hour or two on that duvet!"

"Have you been thrown out?" Tushtots asked.

"Too right," replied Willi Whizkas, " I was so looking forward to a day sleeping."

"Well it's no good looking at me," Tushtots told him, "it's wash day here and I think the vacuum's going to come out too, so I've come outside for a bit of peace and quiet." So Willi Whizkas said good day to Tushtots and ambled wearily off to lie on his nest under the fir trees. It had only just stopped raining, the dripping rainwater made it cold, damp and uninviting, so he sighed miserably and decided to mooch round the gardens hoping something would turn up, and turn up it did. For once Willi's luck was in, the greenhouse door in Jacko the Jack Russell's garden had been left open. Now greenhouses are wonderful because they always seem to be warm inside, even on dull days, and there was a lovely patch of warm soil between the tomato plants. It took Willi Whizkas no time at all to creep in, make himself comfortable and doze off. He slept until teatime, when he woke to the sound of the door sliding to and clicking shut. Not daring to move just in case Jacko should see him, he carefully opened one eye and peeped between the leaves to see what was happening, but nothing was happening because it had already happened! Willi Whizkas was shut in the green house! There was a small window at the top of the greenhouse which was open, but he could never jump up high enough. He was well and truly shut in, unless he could find a way out, he was there for the night, with no food! He paced round the greenhouse a couple of times just to confirm what he suspected, he was well and truly trapped!

Willi Whizkas would just have to sit it out and wait to see what the morning would bring. When he woke up again it was dark and raining. Willi heard scratching, scraping sounds, which he immediately identified as Jacko doing his business before bedtime. The dog trotted up to the greenhouse and started sniffing at the closed door, so Willi Whizkas flattened himself as low as he could, even stopping breathing in case Jacko could smell his breath. Jacko sniffed at the door again and let out a low growl followed by a couple of short yaps.

"Shut up Jacko, and get back in here," called his owner. Jacko had one last sniff before raising his back leg to piddle on the glass, then his claws clattered on the concrete path as he trotted back to the kitchen door. Willi Whizkas breathed a sigh of relief, that should be it until morning, which gave him time to work on his escape plan. He thought and thought, but the more he thought, the more tired he became, soon he was fast asleep.

When the dawn chorus woke him the first thing he saw through the glass was Tushtots and Ginger Tompkins sitting on the wall peering in at him laughing at his predicament.

"This should be interesting," Ginger Tompkins commented to Tushtots, "you just wait till Jacko comes out and finds him in his greenhouse, then we'll see the fur fly!!"

"Don't you feel sorry for him Ginge?" Tushtots asked, "you wouldn't like to be in there."

"I wouldn't have been stupid enough to go in there in the first place, but then Wills never was very bright. Still, look on the bright side," Ginger Tompkins said reassuringly, "He can look after himself, he should easily be able to outrun Jacko."

"But what if he's cornered?" Tushtots asked, still a little concerned for Willi Whizkas.

"Well, he'll just have to be quick off the mark then won't he?"

To make Willi's plight even more painful, he could hear his name being called and a packet of cat biscuits being shaken. Food was not Willi's main concern at that moment as Jacko had just reappeared and was piddling on a lavender bush, after which he turned his back on the bush, made a few growling noises then scratched at the grass with his hind legs.

"Don't dig my lawn up Jacko you naughty dog," yelled Jacko's human, causing Jacko to scamper off down the path towards the green house!

Willi Whizkas began to feel a little uneasy, but he'd nothing to worry about because at that moment Jacko spotted Tushtots and Ginger Tompkins on the wall. Both cats turned around and dropped their tails over the wall, the tips just out of reach of Jacko's snapping mouth as he jumped up and down.

"This seems to be working," announced Tushtots, "it seems to be taking his attention away from the greenhouse."

"See them off Jacko, there's a good dog," Jacko's human commanded, he didn't like cats as they were always scratching holes in his vegetable plot. The human picked up a clump of earth and threw it at the tormenting toms, who scarpered, which left Willi Whizkas very much on his own. At this time of the year the human watered the tomato plants in the greenhouse every morning, which was just what he was about to do. Willi Whizkas crouched as low as he could, trying to hide behind sparse vegetation as his heart thumped deep in his chest. His plan was to shoot out of the greenhouse like a rocket as soon as the door was opened, then over the wall to safety, but he hadn't reckoned on Jacko coming in the opposite direction at exactly the same time, which is precisely what happened. Willi Whizkas turned tail and ran to the back of the greenhouse with Jacko in hot pursuit. Jacko was a nippy little dog, but he was also very clumsy, as he began to chase Willi Whizkas round and round the greenhouse, the tomato plants were trampled, potted petunias were sent flying and plant pots crashing. Jacko's owner couldn't believe his eyes, all his hard work lay in ruins, even his prize-winning cucumber seedlings were beyond redemption. The human yelled at Jacko to stop, but it wasn't over yet. Willi Whizkas, seeing a chance of escape, shot between the man's legs then out through the open door with Jacko at his heels, but luckily just as Willi Whizkas was belting through the greenhouse door the man was trying to close it so that he could teach that horrid cat a thing or two by emptying his watering can on him. Jacko arrived at the door just as it closed, causing him to hurtle headlong through a pane of glass in the door. Willi Whizkas had thought his number was up, but he was over the wall before Jacko had picked himself up and dusted off the broken glass. Luckily for Jacko he was completely uninjured, apart from his pride.

By the time the human had finished swearing and cursing, Willi Whizkas was home and dry. All this hadn't gone unnoticed, Tushtots and Ginger Tompkins had been peeking over the wall, they were now splitting their sides laughing!

"Do you think Willi's lost another of his lives?" Tushtots asked.

"No, but I think Jacko did!"

"Come on," commanded Tushtots, "it's safe to run across the garden, let's go and see how Wills is." Willi

Whizkas was still panting and looking a little dishevelled when the cats caught up with him.

"Well done Wills," applauded Tushtots, "what a performance, I've never seen a cat do so much damage!"

"Well, it wasn't all my fault," protested Willi Whizkas, "that clumsy dog did most of it. Anyway, what was that awful crash behind me as I ran out of the greenhouse?"

"You didn't turn round to see?" Asked an astonished Ginger Tompkins.

"Certainly not, I was too busy making my escape," retorted Willi Whizkas, so the other two gave him an action replay, word for word, each taking it in turn to add a bit more to the story of Willi Whizkas and Jacko going round and round the greenhouse culminating in Jacko's finest hour as he crashed through the glass door sending shards of glass all over the man's vegetable patch. Willi Whizkas laughed and the other two joined in, it was several moments before Willi Whizkas came to his senses.

"But what of Jacko? Was he covered in blood? Did he cut his ears off?" Willi Whizkas asked curiously.

"He appeared to be perfectly OK to me," Tushtots suggested.

"But his owner was furious," added Ginger Tompkins, "poor old Jacko. I expect he's get a good telling off."

"Oh well," laughed Willi Whizkas, "that'll teach him to chase cats won't it?"

"Anyway," added Tushtots, changing the subject slightly, "what were you doing in the greenhouse to start with?"

"And in Jacko's garden of all places?" Ginger Tompkins added, so Willi Whizkas explained that all he'd wanted that morning was somewhere nice and warm to curl up and snooze.

"Which is precisely what I'm going to do now," announced Willi Whizkas, "just as soon as I've had my breakfast, so I won't be receiving callers till tomorrow morning at the earliest," and with that he padded off and miaowed at his kitchen door to be let in.

"There you are Willi you bad lad," said his female human, "why don't you come when you're called? Your tea is still on the floor from last night that you never bothered to come home for."

Willi Whizkas looked down at the dried-up meat from the green can with an attendant bluebottle. It looked exactly the same as the half-eaten breakfasts always did at Gordon's house. He nibbled around the edges imagining he was at Gordon's house stealing Gordon's breakfast, which somehow made it that little bit better. However he was too tired to eat it all so he climbed wearily onto the clean washing in the laundry basket, yawned and was just about to nod off when . . .

"You naughty cat, get off there!" And Willi Whizkas found himself back in the garden again!

24 Walrus Whizkas

Now that summer had arrived Willi Whizkas was spending more and more nights out of doors, he passed one particular Saturday night sitting with Ginger Tompkins swapping stories of past adventures and how they always managed to get out of a scrape in the nick of time. They laughed and laughed at the tale of Willi Whizkas getting locked in Jacko's greenhouse, telling this tale over and over again, which reminded Willi how hungry he had been. Thus breakfast was uppermost in Willi's mind come morning, and luckily the kitchen door was wide open so he ambled in, only to be shushed out by a dripping mop.

"Why do you always come in with muddy paws when I'm doing the floor you bad cat? Go back out until the floor dries and then we'll find you something to eat."

Willi Whizkas sat on the patio patiently and watched the swallows swooping at speeds he could never copy. He'd no hope of ever catching one, but his teeth still chattered with anticipation. His breakfast finally arrived on an old piece of newspaper, but instead of the usual muck it was the leftovers from last nights supper party, which was even worse! He had a sniff, licked a bit of the congealed gravy off a roast potato and decided that if this was the best he was going to get then he'd better look elsewhere. Gordon's leftovers didn't really appeal, so he headed for the police station, but there was no sign of Stinker. He had never ventured past the police station before, but it was a quiet morning and there was nobody about so he thought he would take himself for a walk. He hid under a car when he saw a man walking his labrador, with the Sunday papers in its mouth.

"Stupid dog," thought Willi Whizkas, "he'll be fetching his slippers next!" The Labrador spotted Willi Whizkas under the car, pulled on his lead, wagged his tail and let out a growl, but he was soon pulled away as the lead tightened around his neck. Just then a gust of wind blew a sweet wrapper along the gutter, so just for fun Willi Whizkas chased it, becoming so preoccupied he failed to notice trouble coming his way. 'Trouble' being the name of a huge Rottweiler. Too late to flee, he was trapped in the manic gaze of the dog. As it's black eyes bored deep into him, it's lips started to lift as it bared it's teeth and a little dribble of saliva ran from gleaming fangs. Willi Whizkas froze in fear. The huge beast was only one pounce away, it was too late to arch his back, fluff up his fur or do any of those scary things cats do when they're in a tight spot. The Rottweiler growled menacingly, then let out a deafening bark. Amazingly, Willi Whizkas suddenly heard a voice, calling,

"Stand firm young William Whizkas, don't show him you're scared, his bark's worse than his bite."

But, Willi Whizkas wasn't taking any chances, he shot underneath a car to what he hoped would be safety. Fortunately the Rottweiler was too big to get at Willi Whizkas, so the dog just danced around barking, peering under the car to make sure Willi Whizkas was still there, then barking some more. Now one of two things could happen. The Rottweiler could get fed up and just go away, or, heaven forbid, the car would drive off. Neither of these two possibilities came to pass, however, as the impasse was suddenly broken by a huge black Persian cat who strutted out of an adjacent driveway and faced up to Trouble. The cat and dog knew each other, the dog clearly knew who was boss. The Persian swaggered up to Trouble, let out a loud hiss, and showed a fistful of claws It turned out that Trouble was a bit of a cowardy-custard, and he ran off whimpering.

"Come on young Whizkas, it's safe to come out now," the Persian purred gently, but Willi Whizkas wasn't convinced and looked out from under the car in all directions just to make sure the dog had gone.

"Come on young Whizkas, look lively!" A sharp voice ordered, and Willi Whizkas slunk out from under the car, his tummy very close to the ground.

"There you are young Whizkas, my you've grown into a handsome cat, just look at those magnificent whiskers, just like your father's, he would have been proud of those," the Persian complemented Willi Whizkas.

"You know my name," asked Willi Whizkas quite astonished, "but I don't know who you are."

I'm Hagar," the Persian informed him, "I'm a friend of the family so to speak, but I've not seen you since you were a scrap of a kitten. You don't look much different, just bigger."

"You knew my father?" Willi Whizkas asked.

"Oh yes, I knew Walrus Whizkas very well, we were always playing and having adventures, but your dad had one adventure without me!!"

"What was that?" Willi Whizkas enquired.

"Well, your father had taken quite a shine to a pedigree Maine Coon show cat who was never let outside in case she should meet any run-of-the-mill boy moggies so to speak. Indeed her humans are very, very particular about who she could keep company with, only the best bred tom cats were good enough for her, but your father was only your average everyday moggy. However, he wasn't going to be put off by any of that pedigree nonsense, and would spend many an hour just looking at Clawdia, your mother, through her patio window. She in turn loved your father, but she wasn't allowed out."

"Never allowed out!" Willi Whizkas exclaimed, "that's not fair!"

"Well, she did get out one day," Hagar told him, "and your father was waiting for her and the pair of them ran off together, and, well to cut a long story short young Whizkas, you were one of a litter of six, but you weren't destined to be show cats so you were given away as pets. But you young Whizkas, you were the only sandy-beige cat like your father, all the rest were tabby Maine Coons just like Clawdia. Walrus Whizkas was so proud of you, he would watch you playing with your brothers and sisters through the patio window, I used to join him sometimes, which is how I remember you."

"Oh, I see," Willi Whizkas replied, "I can't really remember. Where are my brothers and sisters now?"

"They were all given away to different humans, I don't suppose you'd know them if you saw them now."

"But what about Clawdia, my mother?" Willi Whizkas begged.

"Well, she carried on being a show cat, she had more kittens, then when her kitten days were over she went to live in a retirement home many miles away."

"And my father Walrus Whizkas, is he still around?"

"I'm afraid not young Whizkas, you see your dad had a very special talent for catching mice and rats. In fact I'd go so far as to say he was fearless when tackling a rat, being able to kill one with just one bite! He was a champion ratter par excellence!"

"Wow." Willi Whizkas, who was pretty hopeless in all departments, was really impressed.

"So when Walrus' humans moved abroad, he was handed to a bacon factory, as far as I know, he's still on rat patrol doing what he likes best. Now then young

Whizkas, what about yourself? You obviously didn't go far from here when you were a kitten."

"No," replied Willi Whizkas, "not far at all, I don't normally go past the police station, having seen the size of that big dog, I know why!!"

"The trick with dogs is to show them who's boss by making out that you're bigger than you actually are and that you are ten times more ferocious than any dog, followed by a quick smack on their nose!"

Willi Whizkas then told Hagar all about himself, who he lived with, who his pals were and what mischief they got up to.

"Things haven't changed a lot young Whizkas, we used to get up to all that when Walrus Whizkas and I were younger. I'm glad 'swot the bluebottle' is still a popular game with you boys, but our favourite game was 'snaffle the spider', this was a game we would play when the cold nights of autumn were with us and big house spiders would come indoors and climb the wallpaper or scuttle across the carpet. It drives humans berserk, especially female humans. So the beauty of this game, young Whizkas, is to watch humans squirm at the sight of the spider, then you become the hero by pouncing on the spider, but not too quickly, it's better to pretend it's difficult to catch, then you get a treat afterwards for being so brave!"

"That sounds like a good idea," enthused Willi Whizkas, "but my humans generally just roll a newspaper up and splat the spider!!"

"Well that doesn't sound much like fun," growled Hagar, "Humans! What about budgie baiting? Have you tried that one young Whizkas?"

"Tell me more," begged Willi Whizkas, who was totally enchanted by Hagar. "What's budgie baiting all about?"

"Well young Whizkas, some old male humans like to keep budgies in the garden. These are brightly coloured birds with long thin tails, not much meat on them mind. All they do all day is chatter to one another and fly back and forth in a large wire cage about the size of a greenhouse which is called an aviary."

"Gosh, I've never seen anything like that," whispered Willi Whizkas in amazement.

"The trick is, young Whizkas, to sneak up to the aviary and climb onto the wire mesh and then look down at the birds and drool; the birds go absolutely wild, scattering in all directions, making a racket! It's great fun seeing so many confused birds flying about, but it doesn't usually last long, because the human who keeps the birds always seems to come out and chase you away. Walrus Whizkas and I had great times together, I do miss him."

"So who do you have adventures with now?" Willi Whizkas asked.

"Well, young Whizkas, to tell you the truth, when a cat gets to a certain age he just likes to curl up on a nice warm lap and reminisce, especially on cold nights. You keep in with your humans young Whizkas and be a good cat."

"Hagar, why was my father called Walrus Whizkas?" Willi Whizkas wondered.

"I thought that would have been obvious young Whizkas, he had the most magnificent set of whiskers ever seen on a cat, as well as being as strong as any dog, and as brave as a lion. He was my best friend ever, I still miss him to this day. Well young Whizkas, it must be lunchtime. Sunday lunch is always the best time to be indoors."

"Why's that? I always like to be out and about during the day."

"Well that's a simple one to answer," laughed Hagar, "the humans always cook a big meal on Sundays, there are very often tasty scraps to be had, especially if you sit by the table looking cute and appealing!"

"Looks like I've got a lot to learn," Willi Whizkas sighed.

"It comes with age and experience, you'll be as old and as wise as me one day young Whizkas," chortled Hagar, with that he bade Willi Whizkas good-bye and told him to find him again one day, and maybe, just maybe, they'd have an adventure together. He told him to look for the house with windows in the roof, and mentioned that he liked to get up into those windows so he could keep an eye on the birds. Willi Whizkas turned then padded off towards his home, delighted to know a bit more about his family. He thought about what Hagar had said and decided to try his luck with the Sunday roast, so he ambled in through the kitchen door to be greeted by the most pungent aroma. Willi Whizkas had never smelt anything quite like it, but assumed this must be the famous Sunday lunch.

"Hello mog-bag, there you are, it's not like you to be in at this time, especially on a Sunday. Try a bit of this."

Willi Whizkas opened his mouth and a piece of curried chicken was popped in. He spat it out in disgust then flicked his tongue several times in an attempt to get rid of the evil taste, then went to his water bowl to wash his tongue and soothe his throat.

"That's the last time I take anyone's advice about food," he grumbled to himself. "I'll just stick to having more adventures and telling tall tales."

25 Nurse Willi Whizkas

Willi Whizkas, up and about early, was most surprised when he got called back to the house. Apparently he'd forgotten to try out the new breakfast food which had come as a free sample through the letterbox the previous day.

"Come on Willi," he was encouraged, "I've got something new for you to try today," as a plain yellow sachet was torn open, the semi-fluid contents were oozed out onto an old saucer, "Looks disgusting, but we'll let you be the judge of that."

It was different all right, the gravy was absolutely delicious, so he licked it all up until only a few solid lumps remained. His human came back into the kitchen five minutes later, only to give him a mild scolding.

"Oh, you useless cat, I see you've done your usual trick, you've licked all the gravy and left the meat. Well I don't think we'll be buying any of that." Willi Whizkas was just moving into the face-washing mode which generally followed a meal when the doorbell rang. Now Willi hated hearing the doorbell because it usually meant strange humans coming into the house, he was often unsure what strangers were going to do. Humans were funny creatures, they either loved cats or hated them. Willi Whizkas thought he recognised the voice of the woman who lived next door, the little girl's mother. The front door closed and Willi's human came back to the kitchen carrying another pouch of the free sample cat food.

"The little girl's mother sent you her sample of cat food, but I expect you'll only eat the gravy again, oh Willi, it appears that you are in demand today." The human's words meant nothing to him, it was only actions that he understood, but he knew all to well what was coming when the nail clippers came out of the odds-and-ends drawer.

"Time for your lazy-cat claws to have a trim Mogbag, then you're going visiting."

After a few snips with the nail clippers accompanied by a good deal of wriggling and yowling from Willi Whizkas he was given a brisk brush and told what was to happen next.

"The little girl next door isn't very well, Willi. She has a nasty dose of the chicken pox, so she's tucked up in bed feeling very sorry for herself, the only thing she is asking for is . . . you Willi Whizkas. The little girl would like you to stay with her for a while," with that he was firmly grasped under the arm of his human and bundled round to the house next door.

"Here we are," said his human, "here's nurse Willi Whizkas. I'll leave him with you, but if he starts miaowing to go out it's probably best if you let him, we don't want him making any messes." Willi Whizkas was carried gently upstairs to the little girl's bedroom where he could see the shape of a small figure hidden under the bedclothes.

Slowly the little girl emerged from under the duvet. She took Willi Whizkas quite by surprise, as instead of her usual sparkling eyes, rosy cheeks and neatly combed hair a scruffy pale little girl covered in red spots blinked wearily at him.

"Oh, Willi Whizkas you've come," she croaked, "I've got to stay in bed all week because I've got chicken pox." The bedroom door was closed and Willi Whizkas was left all alone with the little girl. He did what all cats do when put in a strange room, briefly checking everything out before walking up the bed and wiping his damp nose on her cheeks, all the while purring gently. Deciding to explore properly, he climbed on to her bedside cabinet then decided to put his nose into her glass of water to take a couple of sips. It was exactly the same as the water he got at home, he much preferred to drink dirty water from a puddle or the fish pond. He found the dressing table next, but as he leapt up and landed he came fact to face with another cat staring back at him. Willi's tongue curled as he let out a loud hiss, which, strangely, the other cat also did at exactly the same time, then the penny dropped, he was looking at himself in a mirror! He should have been used to mirrors, there was one just like it in the bedroom at home, but he was banned from the bedroom, so he hadn't seen it that often. There were some small bottles of perfume under the mirror, so he sniffed at each one in turn, but the contents didn't agree with him and he let out a loud sneeze, spraying snot onto the mirror.

"Oh, Willi Whizkas you are funny!! Come and sit on the bed with me." She patted a hand on the duvet to beckon Willi Whizkas, who was glad to oblige, since it was a warm comfortable duvet and he liked the little girl. He duly curled up and her little fingers started to comb through his fur. She felt a little bit better and sang a little song telling him all about how magnificent he was, what big shiny eyes he had and how marvellous his whiskers were. Soon Willi Whizkas and the little girl were fast asleep, only waking when lunch arrived, which consisted of a bowl of soup, freshly buttered toast and a glass of warm milk for the little girl, and a dish of cat biscuits for Willi Whizkas.

"How are you two getting on?" Asked the little girls mother.

"All right," she replied, "but nurse Willi Whizkas had a nasty sneeze onto the mirror."

"Never mind," chuckled the mother, "as long as that's all he does!! If he looks like he wants to go out to the toilet knock on the floor and I'll come and get him." Willi Whizkas crunched away at the cat biscuits which were spreading out on the duvet as the little girl slurped noisily at her soup, having completely forgotten about the glass of warm milk. Willi Whizkas, however, hadn't forgotten about it at all, he walked across the little girl's pillow and on to the bedside cabinet to investigate. He purred with pleasure at the warm sweet aroma, but as he went to lick it he was surprised to find that it wasn't wet at all as a thick skin had formed on top of the milk. He could tell it was going to be delicious so he pushed his snout firmly into the glass only to spring back rapidly as the little girl shrieked with laughter. Willi's face was covered in the thick white skin from the milk! He tried to wipe it off with a paw, but soon his face and paws were coated with bits of the skin which were drying quickly on his fur! The more he shook his head and snorted to clear his nose, the more the little girl laughed.

"I'll put some milk in the bottom of my soup bowl for you," she told him. Willi Whizkas had been right, the milk was truly delicious, when the bowl was empty he looked up at the little girl for more and started licking frantically around his mouth and whiskers to get an extra taste.

"Do you want some more?" She asked, "you are a greedy cat, but I don't like warm milk, you can have as much as you like." Willi Whizkas slurped down all he could before letting out a little burp.

When lunch was over and Willi's face and whiskers were as clean as they were going to get, it was time for another explore. The wardrobe caught his attention this time, there was just enough of the door open for him to push his nose through, so he climbed inside. It was almost dark, but that wasn't a problem for Willi Whizkas, with his cats-eye vision. He could see the little girl's shoes and sandals, and being fond of the smell of leather, not to mention the smell of feet, he gave them a really good sniff, after which he got his head stuck in a little red Wellington boot, so he had to walk backwards in order to dislodge it. The little girl could see what he was doing and it started laughing all over again. He then climbed up to where her school jumpers were neatly folded and, purring, his paws started padding up and down as if he was doing the washing.

"Come on Willi Whizkas, come out of there now," called the little girl, to encourage him she wriggled her fingers under the duvet trying to make it look like there was a mouse in the bed. This caught his attention straight away, in one great pounce he leapt onto the bed and sank his teeth hard into the soft duvet, which of course the little girl couldn't feel. Willi's eyes were wild as she wriggled her fingers from side to side under the duvet, he hadn't had so much fun in ages, . . . and what's more neither had the little girl who thought that Willi Whizkas was much more fun than Archibald the rabbit. It crossed the little girls mind that she might ask her mother if she could have a cat all of her very own, just like Willi Whizkas. After they both became tired of the game, Willi Whizkas decided to wash his bottom, the little girl watched him for a while, but she started to feel tired again, she closed her eyes as Willi Whizkas pulled a few knots out of his fur and spat them out onto the duvet.

"What next?" Willi Whizkas thought to himself. No-one seemed to be in a hurry to put him outside, the little girl loved him and he had a full tummy, but there were still things to be discovered in the bedroom. The little girl's dolls pram in which he had shared a ride with

Archibald the rabbit was in the corner of the room. He remembered it well, having been wrapped in a towel then pushed up and down while the little girl pretended that they were her baby dolls. He climbed warily into the pram, half expecting to find Archibald there, but all that was there today was a little pink doll with yellow hair and long thin legs. He was in two minds whether to spray the little doll but thought better of it as he didn't want to upset the little girl.

"That's more or less it," thought Willi Whizkas as his exploring came to an end. "I've been on the bedside cabinet, in the wardrobe and in the doll's pram."

The only thing he hadn't really done was look out of the window, so he jumped up onto the window ledge. He was immediately taken with the view, he could see the whole of his own garden and beyond that Tushtots' garden, from where Tushtots was at that very moment squeezing under the hedge onto Willi Whizkas' lawn.

"I bet he's looking for me," thought Willi Whizkas, "I've been here all day long and I haven't seen any of my pals."

But how was he going to get out? It was a strange house, he wasn't quite sure where everything was, so he decided to go for the tried and tested method of clawing at the bottom of the door, which soon woke the little girl up.

"What are you doing?" She asked. He looked round at her, miaowed, looked at the door then miaowed again.

"Oh, you want to go out," she guessed, and opened the door. He went through and padded onto the landing. The window was open, Willi Whizkas had escaped from windows before, but this could be a long way down so he went to investigate.

Things couldn't have worked out better, the window overlooked the garage below, so he would only have to jump a couple of metres onto the flat roof, then onto the ground. The only fly in the ointment was a vase of artificial flowers slap-bang in the middle of the windowsill, just where he needed to be to escape. There was only one thing for it, he would have to squeeze past the flowers and hope for the best. Unfortunately, because the flowers were not real there was no water in the vase which made it very top heavy, so that it required the merest touch from Willi Whizkas to send the vase crashing down the stairs. The noise terrified him so much that he was on the garage roof in a flash, then down and across the lawn and back in his own garden before the last piece of pottery had come to rest at the bottom of the stairs. Willi's eyes were wild, his tail was bushed up and his excitement was plain for Tushtots to see.

"Wills, where on earth have you been all morning?" Tushtots demanded, "I've looked everywhere for you."

"I'll tell you in a minute," panted Willi Whizkas, "there's something I really must do first." All that warm milk had finally reached his bladder, so he backed up to his favourite bush with all four paws together and sprayed with a flourish, a smile of relief on his face!.

"That's better," sighed Willi Whizkas, "now, have I got a tale to tell you Tushtots," so he recounted the morning's events.

"Well I don't think you'll be invited back there again!" Tushtots guessed, "which is a shame, you could have been onto a good thing there. Never mind, there's always a nice warm duvet and a free trial pouch of cat meat waiting to be tested over at my house. Come on Wills, I'll race you!!"

26 Fish & Chips

It wasn't hunger that woke Willi Whizkas on this particular morning, but rather an urgent need to do his business, and the sooner the better. The kitchen door was already open, he sped out into the garden in search of a patch of suitable ground, but the soil was rock hard after days of warm dry weather and he was growing more and more desperate!

Luckily he suddenly remembered that the humans who lived at the bottom of Jacko's garden were having work done that involved a huge mound of nice loose soil, so he set off with some urgency.

He was almost across Jacko's garden before the snappy Jack Russell appeared out of nowhere, but a Jack Russell is no match for a cat on a mission, Willi Whizkas clawed his way onto the safety of the panel fence, from where he jumped down onto a huge mound of lovely rich black soil which was soft to the paw and perfect for the job in hand. Much relieved, he returned to his own garden where Ginger Tompkins was waiting for him. Ginger enquired if he'd had any trouble with Jacko.

"Not at all," boasted Willi Whizkas, "I don't think Jacko will ever catch me," but Ginger Tompkins was sure Willi Whizkas' luck would run out sooner or later.

"There's some quite serious gardening being done in that garden, I think there may be some little adventure to be had old chap," grinned Ginger Tompkins. They collected Tushtots on the way to Ginger's garden, as it was easy enough to get a good view of the proceedings from there. The workmen has just started their day's work with a mug of tea and a cigarette but they soon set to work digging a massive hole.

"That's well and truly covered my efforts over!" Willi Whizkas laughed.

"What do you think they want to dig such a big hole for?" Tushtots asked curiously.

"Beats me," replied Willi Whizkas.

"You'd have a job getting out if you fell in, chaps," added Ginger Tompkins. The men carried on digging until they disappeared for their lunch break.

"Let's go and have a look old fruits," suggested Ginger Tompkins, "perhaps if we get a closer look we might be able to work out what it's for." So all three cats climbed down from the fence and went over to the earth works, where the newly-dug soil smelt strange, having been buried under the garden for years. It was almost as if some horrible gas was seeping from it.

"Look at the size of this worm," exclaimed Willi Whizkas as an earthworm almost as long as his tail came wriggling out of the soil.

"Look at this," shouted Tushtots, "look at all the legs on this thing." The cats had never seen a centipede before and watched fascinated as all its legs marched along. Soon the cats were scouring the mound in search of unusual insects, but there wasn't much else to see apart from a big black shiny beetle who had lost his footing and cart wheeled down into the hole. The cats peered into the hole as the beetle tried to scramble out, but every time he got so far then he tumbled back in again.

"Can cats eat beetles?" Tushtots asked, "it would be a handy little snack if we could."

"I've never tried," replied Willi Whizkas.

"I have chaps," Ginger Tompkins butted in, "they

taste absolutely horrid, even the stuff in the green cat meat can tastes better than a beetle."

At that moment the workmen arrived back in the garden so the cats scarpered, but they kept an eye on things all afternoon in between catnaps. Ginger Tompkins woke the other two up from such a nap when something really interesting started to happen. The workmen stretched out an enormous black rubber sheet over the hole, then one of the men jumped in and pressed it down while another placed stones around the edges. Meanwhile the mound of soil was gradually transformed into flower beds, following which a hose pipe appeared.

"I know what it is, I know what it is, I should have known from the start," exclaimed Willi Whizkas excitedly. "It's going to be a pond!!"

"Well you were a bit slow there old thing," laughed Ginger Tompkins, "you've got a pond in your garden."

"I know," Willi Whizkas agreed, "but I've never seen it without water, I always thought the water just went down and down into the earth."

It took the rest of the afternoon and well into the evening before the pond was full, but by the following day the workmen had planted the mound, rolled out new turf and there were even some plants in the pond.

"Now that looks like a pond," Willi Whizkas announced, "I'd have known straight away what it was if it looked like that!!" Tushtots, who liked a drink of water at any time of the day padded over the newly-planted garden to the water's edge and began to lap. A lot of cats close their eyes while they're drinking, Tushtots was no exception, but when he opened his eyes again he stopped lapping, his jaw dropped and his whiskers froze. There was another, large pair of eyes in the water looking back at him, and a big gaping mouth which started to blow bubbles. When he came to his senses Tushtots sprang back and let out a loud hiss.

"What is it Tushtots?" Called the other two as they couldn't see anything to hiss about.

"Come and look at this," stuttered Tushtots, hardly able to get the words out. Willi Whizkas and Ginger Tompkins stood on either side and looked deep into the water.

"I can't see anything," stated Willi Whizkas, "I think you're imagining things!"

"But it was there, it was huge, it had eyes as big as your cat meat saucer Wills, and it was blowing bubbles at me!"

"What was old thing?" Ginger Tompkins demanded.

"Was it a goldfish like I have in my pond?" Willi Whizkas wondered.

"A bit like that," pondered Tushtots thoughtfully, "but this was huge, it would eat your goldfish whole Willi." Willi Whizkas and Ginger Tompkins didn't quite know what to make of Tushtots' fishy story, if there had been a monster fish in the pond, it certainly wasn't there now.

"We'll circle the pond and see if we can see your fish Tusher," Ginger Tompkins insisted, so they looked and looked and then, as if by magic, five, possibly six enormous Koi carp came to the surface right beside the cats. They were all sorts of colours, gold, orange, black and white, with peculiar patches on their scales. It was Willi Whizkas and Ginger Tompkins turn to look in disbelief.

The cats sat down and watched spellbound for what must have been almost an hour as they stared at the magnificent fish swimming round and coming to the surface of the water blowing bubbles before disappearing again.

"I know what you're thinking chaps, but there's no way you're going to get one of those fish out of the water, and if you did what would you do with it?" Ginger Tompkins asked.

"The challenge is just to get one out," muttered Willi Whizkas, not taking his eyes off the fish. But their thoughts were soon distracted when the human who owned the fish came into the garden and saw the three cats admiring the fish. They weren't sure whether to run or stay, but the man seemed friendly enough. He was carrying a small tub of food for the fish and he came to stand by Willi Whizkas and his pals.

"Come to have a look at my fish have you? It didn't take you cats long to find them," he laughed as he sprinkled some of the food onto the water. In no time at all the fish came to the surface and as they began to eat the food the water bubbled and churned with all the activity and Willi's mouth began to chatter.

"Those are Koi carp," announced the human proudly, "they cost a lot of money so I don't want to see you cats winkle one out," he went on, stroking all three cats in turn. Tushtots rolled over on his back to let the man stroke his tummy.

"Now off you cats go, I don't want to see you digging holes in my borders either, or you and me are going to fall out!"

That night Willi Whizkas couldn't stop thinking about the Koi carp in the nice human's pond, how he was going to get one out and what he was going to do with it when he did. They were much to big for him to eat on his own, but the three mouseketeers might polish one off between them if they were really hungry. He was out in the garden very, very early next day, not even bothering with his breakfast. He went straight over the gardens in the direction of the new pond, but Tushtots and Ginger

Tompkins had beaten him to it, they were sitting on the fence by the pond.

"We've been thinking about your plan Willi Whizkas," they told him.

"What plan is that?" Willi Whizkas asked.

"You know, about catching one of those fish, old chap," Ginger Tompkins replied.

"Do you think they taste all right?" Tushtots asked, "some fish taste wonderful but sometimes they're not very nice, but if they taste like salmon or tuna they'll be O.K. "

"Yes, but if they taste like two week old scampi they'll be awful!" Ginger Tompkins added.

"We won't know until we've caught one," declared Willi Whizkas licking his lips. He was just explaining his plan about how they would attract the fish, then grab one when out of nowhere a large grey bird swooped low over the garden, circled the house then landed right by the pond. It straightened it's neck to its full length and stood on very long thin legs, but its most impressive features were its long dagger-like beak and huge staring eyes. The three cats were paralysed with fear and wonderment, the grey heron was truly an impressive sight. However he wasn't interested in the three cats; his eyes were firmly fixed on the dark water below.

"What do you suppose he's here for?" Tushtots asked in a hushed voice, "it's not us cats, birds eat bird seed, stale bread and things like that." But as they mused the heron's murderous beak flashed into the water and pulled out one of the massive fish.

"He's got your fish Wills," yelled Tushtots, "quick, let's get him," the three leapt from the fence and ran hell for leather across the newly planted borders. The startled heron dropped the fish and took off clumsily into the air, letting out a rasping croak. The hapless fish meanwhile was left flapping by the side of the pool.

"Now that's how you catch fish boys," announced Willi Whizkas proudly as he bent down and sniffed the exquisite specimen.

"Well, that's cheating if you ask me," snorted Tushtots.

"Success is all about being in the right place at the right time," boasted Willi Whizkas smugly. He was just about to sink his fangs into the fish when it flipped over then fell back into the water with a dull sploosh. The commotion hadn't gone unnoticed by the man who'd seen everything from his kitchen window, except he hadn't quite seen everything, he hadn't seen the heron, or the cats chasing after it. So, assuming that Willi Whizkas and his cronies had caught the fish themselves, he ran down the garden bellowing "Shoo, shoo you bad cats!"

They duly scarpered back to Tushtots' garden.

"Well that's gratitude for you," whinged Willi Whizkas, "we saved that fish from the bird and we get fingered for it!"

"You had intended to catch it for yourself," Tushtots reminded him.

"There's always another day," muttered Willi Whizkas darkly under his breath. But how wrong he was. When Willi Whizkas went to inspect the pond a couple of days later, it had been covered over with a fine green netting! Willi Whizkas had, had his chips, . . . But not his fish!

27 Rooster Rustling

One morning Willi Whizkas was especially hungry when he woke up so he made a great deal of fuss of his humans, loving round their legs, letting out lots of plaintive mewing and staring pointedly at his empty cat meat saucer.

"All right, all right, we get the message," surprise surprise, the cat meat in the green can came out of the cupboard as usual, but then his human hesitated and said "no, I'll give you a treat today you undeserving, ungrateful cat," as the green can was exchanged for a blue can.

"There, see how you get on with that." Meanwhile he was stroked along the length of his back, his back legs were lifted gently into the air by his tail. He hated it when his humans did that, if a cat was supposed to hang by its tail then it would have been called a monkey! He ate as much as he could and then sat on the patio washing his paws and whiskers thinking about the day ahead. He decided to go and look for Ginger Tompkins, but couldn't find him anywhere, so he went over the gardens to Tushtots' house. He was out of luck there too, Tushtots had just been given a bath and couldn't go out as he was still damp, so all in all he was at a bit of a loose end. As a last resort he thought about slipping over the road to Gordon's house before he remembered that Gordon had gone to the cattery for two weeks. Willi Whizkas jumped up on to the bonnet of a car and sat rubbing his nose around the car aerial purring to himself.

"There must be something I can do," he thought. He didn't really fancy paying Stinker of the Yard a visit, especially if his breath stank of salami as it usually did. But thinking about Stinker put another idea into his mind. It wasn't much past the police station to Hagar the old Persian cat's territory, he had invited Willi Whizkas to drop by and see him again any time. Thus with a spring in his step and a purpose in mind he leapt from the car and trotted off down the road. He knew when he was getting near the police station as the German shepherd police dog Sergeant Fang was barking in the yard. Willi Whizkas noticed Stinker was tormenting the dog by marching up and down outside its kennel, just out of reach. It wasn't far to go past the police station when Willi Whizkas turned left to look for Hagar's house. Hagar had told him that his was the house with windows in the roof. This made it very easy for him to find, for Hagar was sitting in one of the windows, watching a small sparrow dancing up and down on the roof tiles. It doesn't matter how old a cat is, they still have to look at birds if they can, even if there is no chance of catching one. Willi Whizkas jumped up onto the gate post and looked up at Hagar hoping that he would notice him. An old lady walking down the road saw Willi and stopped to give him a stroke.

"You're a nice pussy, whose cat are you? I've not seen you around here before." She tickled him under his chin, Willi Whizkas happily obliged with a smile and a purr. By the time the old lady had set off down the road again he noticed that Hagar had disappeared from the window, but a few moments later he was padding down the drive to meet Willi Whizkas.

"I didn't think I'd see you again young Whizkas," said Hagar surprised.

"Well you did say to pop by and see you."

"So I did, so I did," agreed Hagar, "let's go into my

garden." Hagar led the way with a slow lazy amble around to the back of the house, where they jumped onto a sun-chair with nice soft cushions. Willi Whizkas was a bit unsure about this because when he jumped onto the chair it began to move slowly back and forth.

"Don't worry about it," assured Hagar, "it will stop in a moment or two. For some reason humans like to swing back and forwards."

"I think it might make me feel sick," Willi Whizkas worried. The two cats sat there for almost an hour as Hagar told him all about Walrus Whizkas and Clawdia, Willi's parents, then Willi Whizkas told Hagar all about the Koi carp and the heron. In the warmth of the afternoon they both dozed off.

When they were eventually woken by Sergeant Fang barking in the distance Willi Whizkas asked Hagar about the rooster rustling that his father Walrus Whizkas used to do with Hagar when they were younger. Hagar told him all about the family of humans that kept chickens and a great big rooster in the garden of a large house next to the football field and how the cats would sneak under the chicken wire to try and catch a chicken for their supper. The hens always managed to flutter away just in time, but sometimes the rooster would turn nasty and chase after Hagar and Walrus Whizkas making loads of clucking and squawking noises. This alerted the human who owned the chickens, he would come out with a powerful water pistol and drench the cats, who hated it! However, if they were lucky and the human wasn't at home 'chase the chicken', or 'rooster rustling' as they called it, could last for quite a while.

"Did you ever catch one and have it for your supper?" Willi Whizkas asked, wide-eyed with excitement.

"We came jolly close a couple of times!" Hagar laughed, "but we never did manage to catch one if the truth be known, young Whizkas. I don't think we'd have known what to do if we did, a chicken is too big and has too many feathers to deal with."

"But it sounds fun all the same," enthused Willi Whizkas with an impish glint in his eye. "Oh, will you take me rooster rustling Hagar?"

"I'm not sure about that," Hagar told him, "I'm a bit too old for all that now, and I'm not sure if the human still keeps chickens."

"Well can we at least go and see?" Willi Whizkas pleaded.

"It'll pass the afternoon if nothing else," Hagar replied, as they made their way to the football field, where Hagar pointed out a rambling old house with an overgrown garden.

"That's it there," he told Willi Whizkas, they skirted around the edge of the football pitch looking into the gardens of houses as they passed by.

"Well bless me," exclaimed Hagar, "I'm sure I can hear chickens clucking."

"Is that what that noise is?" Willi Whizkas asked excitedly; he had never heard chickens before.

"Sounds like we might be in luck," smiled Hagar as the cats quickened their pace.

"This is it," declared Hagar, "but it looks like he's put a lot more chicken wire up since I was last here, I'm not sure that we will be able to get in so easily, young Whizkas."

It was true, shiny new wire mesh completely encircled the garden but there was no obvious way the cats were going to get in. But Willi Whizkas got his first look at a real live chicken through the wire. There was a large wooden shed with dozens of brown chickens scratching away at the earth, periodically stopping to peck at what he could only imagine was something to eat.

"A fine sight and no mistake," observed Hagar, "there's more here now then there used to be and there's no sign of a rooster anywhere."

"How do you know which one's the rooster?" Willi Whizkas enquired, "they all look the same to me."

"Well...." Hagar replied, "once you've seen one you will know, but to give you a clue, he's much bigger than the hens, he'll have a big red fleshy crown on his head, a magnificent set of brightly coloured tail feathers and he goes 'cock-a-doodle-do', not 'cluck cluck cluck' like the hens."

The two cats circled the garden a second time looking for a way in, but there wasn't one. They were about to give up and go home when Willi Whizkas had one of his master plans.

"What about climbing up that tree over there?" Willi Whizkas asked.

"Yes, . . ." said Hagar fearing the worst. "Go on, then what?"

"We shimmy along that branch that goes over the top of the fence, jump down, and hey presto we're in!"

Hagar surveyed the situation and muttered "Hmmm" a lot to himself.

"Well I suppose it might work," he mused after a while, "but it's a long way to jump down."

"It's not much higher than a garage," said Willi Whizkas, "and I've jumped off garages before now. Oh please, please can we do it Hagar?"

Hagar was reluctant at first, but Willi's pleading won through.

"You go first then young Whizkas, as it's your plan." Hagar wasn't sure that the branch would be strong enough to take his weight, but Willi Whizkas was determined to go rooster rustling. He jumped into the tree then carefully tip-clawed his way along the quivering branch

"Go on young Whizkas, not far now," encouraged Hagar, "you're almost there."

The further out along the branch that Willi Whizkas went, the more the branch bent under his weight, as soon as he had cleared the top of the fence the branch snapped and he fell slap-bang into the middle of a group of startled chickens. All hell broke loose, with chickens scattering in all directions squawking and squealing. Hagar looked on fearing the worst, as there was no possibility of escape from the hen pen now that the branch had broken. No such thoughts in Willi's mind though, he was here to chase chickens, and chase chickens was what he was going to do. He was quite surprised how fast chickens could run and even more amazed at how much noise they could make. The more they ran and flapped, the more excited Willi Whizkas became. He dived, pounced, leapt and cart wheeled in hot pursuit of the chickens, but they were always just that little bit too quick for him. Unbeknown to Willi Whizkas, however, all this commotion had woken up the rooster, who'd been sleeping in the hen house, he strutted magnificently outside to survey the scene. The chickens stopped running when they saw the rooster. Willi Whizkas looked up to see one very angry rooster glaring at him, but before he could collect his senses a powerful beak came crashing down on his head followed by another peck, then another. This wasn't fair; he hadn't hurt any of the chickens, and now the rooster was chasing Willi Whizkas, who had nowhere to hide but the hen-house. Inside he was greeted by the overwhelming smell of chicken poo which made his eyes water and stuck to his paws. The rooster didn't follow Willi Whizkas into the hen house, instead he stood guard outside the entrance cock-a-doodle-dooing at the top of his voice. Now as you can guess, all this rumpus hadn't gone unnoticed by the human, who thought a fox had got into the hen pen and been chased into the hen house by the rooster. He decided the only thing to do under the circumstances was to call the police, so a constable from the police station accompanied by a fiercely barking Sergeant Fang duly arrived at the hen house.

"Well done Rooster," praised the chicken owner as he opened the door to the hen house, "that pesky fox must be in there!" Once Sergeant Fang was sent in It took him no time at all to locate a cowering Willi Whizkas hiding in a nest box. Now Sergeant Fang had a score to settle with Willi Whizkas, so this was his big chance. A few loud barks and Willi Whizkas shrank even further into the nest box, accidentally breaking an egg, so that his fur became matted with runny yolk. Just at that moment Sergeant Fang cocked his leg and drenched Willi Whizkas with dog wee just for good measure!!

"I think he's got that fox cornered!" The constable announced, "we need a strong box to put him in." To the relief of the constable and chicken owner it wasn't a fox that Sergeant Fang escorted from the hen house, but one stinking soggy moggy who was more than happy to go into the box out of the way of a slavering Sergeant Fang! Hagar, meanwhile, who had been watching from the safety of the tree, assumed the worst for Willi Whizkas, so he was very relieved to hear a few distressed yowls coming from the box. Once safely inside a police cell the box was opened, Willi Whizkas emerged only to hide under the bed and whimper. Outside in the yard Stinker heard something going on, he jumped onto the windowsill to see who the culprit was. He couldn't believe his eyes when he saw a bedraggled Willi Whizkas looking very sorry for himself. Willi Whizkas was scanned for an identity chip and in no time at all his humans were located. They couldn't believe what they were hearing, having no idea he ever wandered off so far or got up to such naughty mischief!

He was bundled into his basket and taken home in disgrace, where he was made to submit to the greatest indignity any cat can suffer; a long hot bath! Well, something had to be done about the egg yolk and dog wee!

And so a chastened but sweet-smelling Willi Whizkas was grounded for a week.

28 Catflap Crashers

Willi Whizkas awoke from a deep sleep to the sound of caterwauling outside his patio window, he leapt up expecting to see a cat fight but it was just Ginger Tompkins trying to attract his attention. It had obviously worked, so Willi Whizkas stood up and miaowed loudly to be let out.

"Be quiet you noisy cat! You've not been in that long, I'm trying to watch the football," his male human snapped. Luckily, the half-time whistle blew, so the patio window was slid open and he was pushed outside. Willi Whizkas and Ginger Tompkins touched noses then sniffed each other, and Willi asked Ginger what, if anything, was happening.

"Well . . ." replied Ginger Tompkins, "your humans have been round to feed me today. There is no sign of my humans and their suitcases are missing so putting two and two together I think my humans have gone off on holiday and forgotten to put me in the cattery."

"It can't have been a mistake," assured Willi Whizkas, "you have your own cat flap so they obviously trust you to come and go."

"It would appear so old fruit," agreed Ginger Tompkins after a moment's thought, "so feel free to pop over any time."

"Have you got any food left?" Willi Whizkas hungrily asked.

"Yes . . . a bit," Ginger Tompkins confirmed.

"I'll come and help you finish it off," drooled Willi

Whizkas. It was quite spooky being in the house all on their own, having the freedom to explore anywhere they liked. Willi Whizkas discovered a superb view of the garden where Jacko lived, he then had a mad moment jumping up and down on the bed before exploring the rest of the house.

When the exploring had been concluded and the remains of Ginger Tompkins' meal polished off the customary whisker and paw washing took place. Willi Whizkas was suddenly struck with one of his master plans.

"It's like this Ginge...." began Willi Whizkas not knowing quite how to put his idea across, "you're sort of on your own here with your humans away . . ."

"Yes old sausage . . ." replied Ginger Tompkins, sensing that something was about to be revealed.

"What if we had a pussy-party?" Willi Whizkas suggested. "You, me, Tushtots and Gordon, we could play games and things."

"Go on . . ." said Ginger Tompkins, "tell me more"

"Well," ventured Willi Whizkas, now in his element, "we could all sit on the bed and swop favourite tales, we could have a curtain climbing competition and races up and down the stairs."

"Sounds good to me old thing," enthused Ginger Tompkins, "but I don't think Gordon will be up to anything energetic after his accident."

"Well he can keep score then Ginge," suggested Willi Whizkas. "You go and see Gordon and I'll go and see Tushtots and we'll all meet up after dark."

Willi Whizkas was excited all day just thinking what they might do. He certainly fancied his chances in the curtain climbing competition. It had been one of his favourite activities as a kitten until the curtains were replaced with vertical blinds. After an unexpected treat in the shape of a tin of sardines for his tea, Willi Whizkas was beginning to feel well and truly in the party mood, he couldn't wait to go round to Ginger Tompkins' house. All four cats met up after dark as planned, they agreed that a party was a wonderful idea. Willi Whizkas glowed with inner pride as it was his idea in the first place.

"What shall we do first?" Gordon asked, "nothing too energetic I hope?"

"Well," suggested Willi Whizkas, "what about a bit of story telling on the duvet, that's not very energetic?" So Gordon began to tell them all about the day the parrot escaped from his cage and how close he had come to catching it and having it for his supper.

"So what stopped you?" Tushtots asked, intrigued by the tale.

"Slippery table cloth," replied Gordon. "The bird landed on one end of the table so I pounced onto the other end in hot pursuit, but instead of catching the bird the cloth slipped from under my paws on the polished wood and I ended up in a heap on the floor, covered in knives, forks, vinegar and a dollop of tomato ketchup. Of course my humans came running in to see what the commotion was all about only to find that the bird had gone back in it's cage and the door had closed behind it!"

"Too clever by half these cage- birds," mumbled Willi Whizkas.

"But even worse than that," grumbled Gordon, "I was put outside and missed my supper!" The cats all giggled and sniggered as one by one they all told tall tales, but of course nothing could top Willi's story about being arrested for rooster rustling and taken in for questioning. He was still very embarrassed by the recent incident, but it did make for a good story. Stair racing came next, but Gordon decided to sit this one out.

"You'll have to be judge then," Willi Whizkas pointed out.

"How are we going to do this?" Tushtots asked.

"Well, the three of us will have to race together," Willi Whizkas told him, "we'll start in the hall, up the stairs, around the bend, across the landing, jump onto the bed, jump off again, then back down the stairs. It's the first one back to the doormat who's the winner."

"It's a bit unfair," Ginger Tompkins complained, "whoever has the inside lane has the shortest distance to run."

"Hmmmm" replied Willi Whizkas, "I think it will have to be the youngest on the outside to make it fair," with that they lined up. However, Willi Whizkas lied about his age and stole the inside lane which of course should have gone to Ginger Tompkins.

"I'm going to raise my paw," announced Gordon, "and when I lower it that's your signal to start, and may the best cat win!"

They were off. When they got to the bend they were neck and neck, but Willi Whizkas got ahead by a whisker on the landing he maintained his lead until they got to the bedroom. However, just as Willi Whizkas was about to leap off the bed Ginger Tompkins crashed into him sending him spinning onto the floor in a daze. Keen to take the advantage Tushtots made a clean leap over the pair of them and sped back across the landing in a flash. Back to their senses now Willi Whizkas and Ginger Tompkins chased after Tushtots, who went too wide round the bend allowing the other two to catch up, it was nose to nose as they started the long flight of stairs down to the hall. Gordon gasped in disbelief at the sight of three cats hurtling towards him. With only five stairs to go Willi Whizkas sprang, hoping to reach the mat first, but he misjudged his jump and crashed onto the hall table sending the telephone and a bowl crashing to the ground. Ginger Tompkins and Tushtots, neck and neck, crossed the finishing line as one. Gordon couldn't choose between the two of them in the end, but as it was Ginger Tompkins' house and Ginger Tompkins' party Gordon thought it was only fair to declare him the winner. Tushtots wasn't happy with this decision so an argument broke out, paws were raised and they growled at each other. Willi Whizkas didn't help matters by saying it looked like a draw to him, but Gordon was having none of that. However the argument was soon forgotten when they heard the cat flap rattle, they went to investigate. Ginger Tompkins, who was first on the scene spotted Thugsby's head poking through the cat flap looking at him.

"Evening lads," chirruped Thugsby boldly, "heard you·was having a party, so the more the merrier I thought!"

"Oh, err, um" stuttered Ginger Tompkins, "we'd only planned on the four of us."

"Well one more won't hurt," replied Thugsby, "so what are you doing, playing games or what?"

"We've just had a stair race," Tushtots breathlessly announced, "which I'm sure I won!"

"Quiet!" Gordon snapped, "I'm the judge!"

"So what's next on the agenda?" Thugsby demanded, then to everyone's surprise a thin dirty white female cat appeared through the cat flap, followed by two more females and a battered tom.

"You remember Rumpuss, Broozer, Badpuss and Grunter don't you?" Thugsby asked, as one by one the uninvited guests arrived in the kitchen. In no time at all the kitchen was full of cats all out for an evening of fun.

"Oh dear," whispered Tushtots, "I'm not sure I like the look of this lot, they look a bit rough."

"They're all right really," Willi Whizkas assured him, "they're the sort of cats you need when you're in a tight spot." The next game was to be curtain climbing, the tall floral curtains having been closed by the humans before they left for their holiday.

"Perfect," announced Badpuss, soon there were nine cats clawing their way up Ginger Tompkins' human's best curtains. Threads were pulled and dirty paws left grubby marks, it was great fun while it lasted. Alas! The extra weight of nine revelling cats soon brought the whole lot crashing to the ground, covering the competitors in a tangled heap of curtains. Now the fun started, to see who could find their way out. The lounge was turned into a writhing mass of cats and curtains. Willi Whizkas found his way out, but it was such good fun he went back in again! It was terrific sport and carried on until every cat was exhausted and overheated.

"I feel a bit sick now," Broozer, moaned, before coughing up a huge fur ball onto the carpet. "That's better," she said cheerily.

"I don't think it will be for me," moaned Ginger Tompkins glumly, "I'm going to get the blame for that." But before he had chance to dwell on it the game changed to 'tick', everyone went tearing after Rumpuss who ran across the sideboard knocking off ornaments and framed photographs as she was chased over the back of the sofa, across the hall then up the stairs by eight overexcited cats. It wasn't so much a race as a stampede as the game disintegrated into full scale mayhem with cats running in every conceivable direction. Everything that could be knocked over was. One cat tried to climb up the wallpaper in the dining room, but he was just reducing it to shreds. An outbreak of claw sharpening followed, the sofa being the victim. Ginger Tompkins couldn't believe his eyes, things were rapidly getting out of hand and he was starting to panic. He caught sight of Willi Whizkas and cried,

"We've got to get them out of the house Willi," but Willi Whizkas wasn't listening, he'd never had so much fun in his life. After the claw sharpening everyone dashed upstairs, where Grunter announced,

"New game!!"

The new game was to see how far the cats could spray up the bedroom wallpaper, even the girl cats joined in. Things had gone too far now, Ginger Tompkins was getting very, very angry, shouting "party's over. I'm afraid I'm going to have to ask you all to leave" at the top of his voice.

But eight tails were in mid-flourish and they just ignored him.

"I'll run and fetch Stinker of the Yard," thought Ginger Tompkins, then he disappeared at lightening speed. When he returned with Stinker even more damage was being done, burst pillows had scattered downy feathers high into the air, cups and saucers lay smashed on the kitchen floor.

"Right then," bellowed Stinker, "we need to take control of this little lot," and he marched smartly through the house giving out commands. A fight had broken out in the bathroom, and things were beginning to turn nasty, but Stinker soon stamped his authority on the ugly mob and one by one the cats were given a clip round the ear before being marched out into the night until only Willi Whizkas and Ginger Tompkins remained with Stinker.

"Looks like that's all sorted for you, sir," observed Stinker. "Well, I'll leave you to tidy up then," and off he went.

"I'm not sure how you're going to get out of this one Gingey," Willi Whizkas sympathised.

"Thank you very much, this was all your idea Willi."

Just then they heard a key in the front door, and exchanged shocked glances.

"Run for it!" Ginger Tompkins commanded as he flew through the cat flap closely followed by Willi Whizkas, but Willi Whizkas was not quite quick enough: he had been seen, and even worse, identified!

29 Britney Kitney

At last the weather cleared up after several days of grey skies and rain, Willi Whizkas thought it was about time to check out his territory, spray on a few bushes and see what Ginger Tompkins was up to.

"Ay up Ginger, what shall do this morning?" Willi Whizkas asked brightly hoping that Ginger Tompkins might have an idea or two. But Ginger was having none of it.

"Bit too tired, to tell you the truth old chap," yawned Ginger Tompkins. "I've had a night out on the tiles, I need to catch up on a spot of sleep, tomorrow perhaps?" He yawned, his eyes closed, and he was out for the count.

"Charming!" Willi Whizkas muttered, "I'll give Gordon a try, at least he'll be pleased to see me." Gordon was fast asleep too, stretched out under a car

"Hi Gordon," Willi Whizkas called out, "how's tricks?"

"Couldn't be better Willi, there's nothing better than a good snooze after a brilliant night out on the tiles," with that Gordon stretched lazily, yawned and rolled over. Willi Whizkas was most put out, not only had two of his best chums had a night out and not invited him, they were now both too tired to pay him any attention. He stomped back across the road.

"Well I'd better go and see what Tushtots is doing, I suppose he'll be asleep too after a night on the tiles," he grumbled to himself. He nosed his way through Tushtots' catflap and, sure enough, there was Tushtots curled up on an armchair sound asleep! Willi Whizkas jumped onto the back of the chair and looked down at Tushtots's sleeping body.

"Not you as well?" Willi Whizkas grumbled, just loud enough to wake Tushtots from a deep sleep.

"Oh, it's you Willi," yawned Tushtots trying to focus through a pair of sleepy, bleary eyes.

"I suppose you've been out on the tiles too?" Willi Whizkas asked.

"How did you know that?" Tushtots enquired looking rather surprised, "have you been speaking to Ginger Tompkins or Gordon?"

"As a matter of fact I have," Willi Whizkas confirmed sniffily, "and just why wasn't I invited?"

"Well," Tushtots told him, "it's simple, when it stopped raining just after midnight Ginger Tompkins and Gordon came to collect me, they asked if I'd like to have an adventure with them. We did think of you honestly Willi, but all your house lights were off and you don't have a catflap so there was no way we could collect you." It was true, Willi Whizkas was the only cat without a catflap, but that didn't stop him sulking and feeling left out.

"So what did the three of you do that was so special?" Willi Whizkas whinged petulantly.

"We all eventually met up with Thugsby, he's never quite got out of the habit of being an alley cat, he likes to go back now and then, so he took us across to his old stomping ground where we had a midnight feast of scraps from the bins behind the butcher's shop. I had a whole pork pie to myself Wills, Ginger Tompkins found a black pudding but I didn't fancy it myself, Gordon had a sausage then Thugsby had a huge piece of scrag end. By the time we'd finished we had bellies like bullets we were so full. Oh, it was fantastic Wills, then to round the evening off we chased moths in the moonlight, although we weren't very quick after that feast!"

With that Tushtots let out a very loud contented burp. "Sorry, Wills, but I really must catch up on some sleep, I'll see you at teatime."

Willi Whizkas sat on the sofa having a half-hearted attempt at a wash, but he couldn't settle so he wandered off looking for action. The bees were buzzing in the foxgloves, he made a few spirited leaps into the air not really wanting to catch one in case he got stung, but it was the thrill of the chase that made him do it. He glared at the fish in the pond, but they dived down into the murky depths for cover as soon as they saw him. He was beginning to get very bored, for a second his brain took a catnap. But things weren't to stay boring for long as he suddenly noticed a strange noise coming from next door. It was a tinkling bell similar to the many that Willi Whizkas had strapped round his neck to stop him catching birds, although he had always managed to hook the collars off and lose them one way or another. He didn't know of any other cat in his area who wore a bell, so who was muscling in on his patch? He squeezed through the hole in the hedge into the little girl's garden, pausing from his mission to shamelessly fuss round her legs and chirrup in the hope of being given a titbit.

"Oh, there you are Willi," she laughed, "I've got something to show you." She held out a tiny fluffy black-and-white kitten with a little red collar and the tinkling bell that Willi Whizkas had heard. She bent down and held the kitten out for Willi Whizkas to sniff, but he let out a little hiss and raised his paw. "Oh don't do that Willi Whizkas," she pleaded, "she won't hurt you, you big bully. It's my beautiful new kitten, Britney Kitney, I got her for my seventh birthday, Watch what she can do."

She took a piece of string from her pocket and jiggled it up and down while Britney Kitney jumped and leapt and pawed. The little kitten was undoubtedly cute, and very,

very playful, but Willi Whizkas suddenly snapped. He lunged at the tiny kitten, bowling her over and pinning her to the ground as he nipped at her ear letting out a very loud hiss.

"You mustn't do that you bully, she's only tiny. I hate you Willi," the little girl screamed at him as she scooped up the kitten and ran into the house with it slamming the door firmly behind her. Willi Whizkas was feeling more put out than ever, his friends were all asleep, he'd upset the little girl and now there was a new kitten on the block, what was he to do? He moped around for ages, half-hoping that Tushtots or Ginger Tompkins or even Gordon would pop round, but nobody showed up. He finally gave up, curled up in his favourite place on the worktop above the sink and went to sleep.

Next day his mood was a little better. The sun was streaming through the kitchen window, he would have let himself out if he had a catflap, but he had to settle for a wee in his litter tray, then he licked the bottom of the kitchen taps to get a little water, even though there was water in his bowl. As anyone who has kept a cat knows, a cat likes to steal his water. He looked out over the garden watching blackbirds trotting up and down looking for worms. He had tried eating worms for himself, but somehow they didn't have the same appeal as a nice warm bird or a mouse. However a blackbird could eat a worm, Willi Whizkas could eat the blackbird, and that seemed like a pretty good idea to him! When he was eventually let out it was well into the morning, he could hear the little girl next door singing in her high-pitched tuneless way then he remembered Britney Kitney. What a silly name for a cat, he thought, almost as bad as Tushtots. He popped under the hedge to see what the little girl was doing, and to keep an eye on Britney Kitney, but he should have realised where the kitten would be, she was tucked up in the little girl's pram being taken for a walk in the garden!

"Hello Willi," called the little girl, "I hope you're going to behave yourself today, I was very cross with you yesterday." She picked Willi Whizkas up and showed him Britney Kitney, as the kittens pretty blue eyes stared back at Willi Whizkas the cheeky little upstart hissed back at him, much to his surprise.

"Oh you've upset her, I so hoped you'd get on with her," sighed the little girl. "You're the reason why I had her Willi."

Willi Whizkas fussed around for a few moments hoping that the little girl would go and bring out some cat biscuits, he didn't get any so he soon lost interest in Britney Kitney and the little girl. He decided to wander over the road to Gordon's house, where Gordon was sitting in his window looking out.

"Come in, come in," shouted Gordon, "come and sit with me for a while."

"Gordon's fault, Gordon's fault," screeched the parrot in his cage, "burglars, burglars!"

He squawked even louder when he saw Willi Whizkas, but Willi Whizkas took no notice as he jumped onto the window sill and sat at the opposite end to Gordon

"Well, are you better for your sleep?" Willi Whizkas asked sarcastically.

"Much better," replied Gordon, "it's a pity you didn't come with us Willi Whizkas, maybe next time?" The pair of cats gazed out onto Gordon's front garden and the street beyond.

"What's new then Willi?" Gordon asked.

"Well," Willi Whizkas informed him, "I'm not sure if it's going to be good news or not. The little girl who lived next to me has got a new little kitten, it's a black and white number, what's more it's a girl called Britney Kitney."

"Yuk! What a horrid name," gagged Gordon.

"Pretty thing," Willi Whizkas went on, "very small though."

"They soon grow," Gordon told him, "look at you, it wasn't so long ago I remember you as a scrap of a terrified tiny kitten."

"Quite so," remembered Willi Whizkas. "Anyway I showed her right from the start who was boss around here."

"What do you mean?" Gordon enquired.

"Well I just put her in her place, the cheeky little thing had the nerve to hiss at me this morning!"

"Sounds like you asked for it," Gordon suggested, and Willi Whizkas had to agree as they turned their attention back to the goings-on in the street.

"Look, is that her?" Gordon asked, lifting a claw pointing to the little girl's garden. Britney Kitney had somehow managed to give the little girl the slip and came gambolling sideways down the little girl's drive, fur fluffed up and back arched. She started to chase after a leaf which danced in the breeze, and was heading towards the road.

"Oh dear, I don't like the look of this Willi," Gordon wailed, "the silly little thing is going to run into the road after that leaf!" Sure enough, she did! "Come on, we have to do something," and with that the cats dashed through the cat flap and out onto the pavement. Britney Kitney, who was by now in the middle of the road, caught sight of Willi Whizkas and let out a warning hiss.

"I see what you mean, feisty little thing isn't she?" Gordon panted. Willi Whizkas tried to tell Britney Kitney about the dangers of roads and the fact that Gordon had had an accident on that very spot, but the message didn't sink in as the kitten carried on playing with the leaf in the road. The little girl by now had missed the kitten, she had come out to look for her, calling "Puss, puss, puss," whilst tapping on a cat meat saucer with a blunt knife. Britney Kitney was rolling on her back in the road playing with the leaf when Gordon caught sight of a van speeding towards the kitten.

"Quick Willi! Do something," Gordon yelled, without a second thought Willi Whizkas dashed out, grabbed Britney Kitney by the scruff of her neck, then ran to the other side of the road just in the nick of time!! The little girl clasped her hands to her face and was screaming hysterically as her mother arrived on the scene to see the hero of the hour bringing Britney Kitney safely back to the pavement. Tears ran down the face of the little girl as she hugged Britney Kitney to her chest smothering her with kisses.

"Thank you Willi Whizkas," she said as she bent down and gave him a reward kiss on top of his head, "you are a good boy Willi, I'm very sorry that I shouted at you yesterday." He fussed round the little girl's legs, as Britney Kitney looked down at Willi Whizkas and hissed. Gordon looked on, a smile playing around his whiskers.

"That's kittens for you," thought Gordon to himself, "too busy to pay attention to what really matters!" Later that evening there was a knock on Willi's front door. It was the little girl with her mother, they had come to tell Willi's humans all about him saving Britney Kitney from the road and putting his own life at risk, how brave he'd been and that here was a treat especially for him. It was a huge bag of chicken and ham scraps that had been purchased from the same supermarket that Tushtots' humans bought them. Willi Whizkas heard the bag rustle so he ran over to investigate, the little girl sat cross-legged on the carpet and started to feed him a piece at a time, giving him a little stroke now and then. When he had eaten as much as he could force down he managed to slip outside, where, after some serious whisker and paw washing, he sat in the moonlight feeling well and truly pleased with himself, and very, very full.

Ginger Tompkins, Gordon and Tushtots appeared silently as cats do.

"Ah. Willi, you're out old chap," said Ginger Tompkins.

"So??" Willi Whizkas yawned bloatedly,

"We're going to have an adventure, a real night on the tiles if your up to it old thing," Ginger Tompkins went on. Willi Whizkas had been very upset the previous night when he hadn't been invited and was all for it except for one thing.

"I think I'm too full, I've just had an enormous supper. I need a good night's sleep!" And with that he let out a very loud burp!!

30 Snow Blind

The winter nights were drawing in, everyday seemed to be colder and damper. Willi Whizkas, having not quite grown his thick winter coat yet, was beginning to feel the cold, it was more and more difficult to persuade him to go outside. When he did go out it was for just long enough to do his business before racing back inside and curling up in his favourite spot on the worktop above the fridge. When he was put outside for the day if he wasn't in Tushtots' house he was in Gordon's, and failing that he would squeeze through Ginger Tompkins' catflap to seek shelter there. His constant visits were starting to wear a little thin with the other cats' humans, so they were actively discouraging him from coming into their houses, he often found himself out on his own in the chill of winter. He started to look for other places to shelter from the cold, the old garden shed was now quite an attractive place to be as he had made himself a nest on some old carpet behind the bicycles. He wasn't quite sure why his humans had bought the bicycles, they'd had a keep-fit fad which had lasted all of six weeks and the bikes hadn't been used since then!

One cold frosty morning he took a deep breath of the cold air, and felt it burn deep down into his chest before a misty white cloud billowed from his mouth as he breathed out again. He skipped down the path, his attention distracted by a Christmas card robin giving him a curious sideways glance from the clothes line. The robin knew he was much too high for Willi Whizkas to spring up at, so he danced up and down the line taunting and frustrating him.

"Cheeky blighter!" Willi Whizkas muttered to himself, "he wouldn't be so brave if I had him cornered under the bushes!"

His most urgent need now was warmth, so he decided to see if Tushtots would let him share his human's duvet. Unfortunately Tushtots' humans caught him helping himself to Tushtots' breakfast again, and shooed him back out in the cold. Will's mood turned sour, he was cold, hungry and outdoors. What was he going to do? Where was he going to go?

"Best keep on the move," he thought miserably, at least while he was walking he was keeping warm. He walked down as far as the police station thinking that a day in the police cells would be just the ticket, but they were far too busy as ice had caused a lot of accidents and everybody was fully occupied on emergency calls. Even Stinker had no time for him as he was 'busy on police business'.

Willi Whizkas was picking his way back home through the gardens when he had a flash of inspiration. He hadn't been to see the little girl and her kitten, Britney Kitney, for a few weeks, perhaps they would let him in and give him a chance to warm his paws and munch a titbit or two. He looked through the patio windows and saw Britney Kitney, who was almost fully grown by now, with the little girl playing with a ping pong ball. Willi Whizkas couldn't believe his eyes, the kitten had grown into such a pretty cat. He must have stared in through the window for at least ten minutes before Britney Kitney saw him, startled, she gave him a hiss, but when Britney saw it was Willi Whizkas she walked up to the window miaowing a greeting.

"Oh look," exclaimed the little girl, "Willi has come to see us Britney Kitney," sliding the patio window open just enough to let him nose his way in. Willi Whizkas and Britney Kitney touched noses then Britney Kitney reared up on her hind legs waving her paws round like a boxer, so Willi Whizkas pounced, soon the pair were locked in a play-fight rolling round and round the carpet then chasing one another's tails. The little girl laughed and tried to join in, but unfortunately Willi Whizkas bit her finger by mistake and the little girl started to cry, causing her mother to rush in to see what all the fuss was about.

"Hello Willi," she said, "long time no see," but the little girl wasn't badly bitten and she soon forgot about it, which was lucky for Willi Whizkas as he might have been thrown out into the cold again. His hunch paid off, the little girl ran into the kitchen and came back with a packet of cat biscuits. She picked up the two cats and plonked them on the sofa, while she carefully laid out a long line of cat biscuits across the carpet. Then she placed Willi Whizkas at one end of the biscuits and Britney Kitney at the other and waited to see who would reach the middle first eating the biscuits as they went along. The two cats were so engrossed on eating then moving onto the next biscuit that they didn't notice that they were getting closer and closer together. Willi Whizkas was just 'hoovering' the treats up and swallowing them whole, so he soon got to where the little girl thought the middle was, but he didn't stop there and carried on. The little girl stared and wondered what would happen when there was only one biscuit left. She didn't have to wait long, soon the cat's heads bumped, Britney Kitney hissed, then Willi Whizkas reared up and bowled her over and bit her soundly on the neck. Britney Kitney let out a painful squeal and ran behind the sofa.

"Willi Whizkas you are a brute," yelled the little girl, annoyed, "just for that I'm going to put you out!" In a jiffy he found himself outside in the freezing cold again. The bright sun had turned very pale and a thin mist of cloud had started to cover the sky.

"Oh no, not more rain," Willi Whizkas scowled. It was still to early for his humans to be home, so as a last resort he thought he would try his luck across the road at Gordon's house. Gordon was in one of his favourite places, sitting in the window surveying the street with its comings and goings, he beckoned him in with a nod and a twitch of his whiskers. Willi Whizkas was soon sitting alongside Gordon, the radiator below the windowsill letting a flood of warm air circulate round their bottoms. "This is very nice of you Gordon, letting me share. Everyone else seems to be shooing me outside today. You're very lucky that your humans don't go to work any more," said Willi Whizkas enviously.

"That's right," agreed Gordon. The two pals dozed for a while, when they awoke the sky had turned black.

"Don't like the look of that," Gordon observed.

"Could be more rain," Willi Whizkas predicted.

"Unless I'm very much mistaken," purred Gordon, "that's not rain. Look Willi, look up there, I think it's starting to snow!"

Willi Whizkas looked up excitedly, the snowflakes were everywhere, big fluffy white snowflakes which floated down almost like bird's feathers. The cats were mesmerised, they tried following one from the highest point in the sky right down to the ground.

"It's starting to stick," Gordon noticed.

"What do you mean, stick?"

"Well," replied Gordon, who had more experience of these matters, "sometimes snow melts when it lands, other times it sticks to the ground and makes a thick white carpet," which was exactly what it was doing now. Gordon's human put down her newspaper and looked out of the window.

"I think you'd better go now Willi, before it gets too deep for you to find your way home." She opened the window and helped him out into the snow. His paws were colder than ever now, but the snow was good fun!

Then a passing car squirted a shower of slush in Willi's direction, narrowly missing him, so he squeezed through the hedge into his own garden. The snow was coming down thicker than ever, Gordon was right, it was really sticking, almost up to his tummy. The only place to seek refuge was the old garden shed, so he slunk in, shook the snow off, and started to lick his fur dry. Never had the garden shed been so welcoming, he curled up as tight as he could on the old carpet behind the bikes and drifted off into a peaceful sleep. What Willi Whizkas hadn't realised was that the snow was drifting and piling up at the door of the shed.

It wasn't quite dark when he came to, there was an eerie light inside the shed, it almost glowed pale orange. He wasn't really sure if it was time for his humans to be at home or not, so he went to leave through the gap in the shed door, only to realise that he was trapped by a huge mound of snow.

He jumped onto the saddle of one of the bikes and tried to look out of the window, but it was covered in thick old cobwebs, dead spiders and dried-up bluebottles, so he couldn't really see out. He let out a few plaintive mews, but there was no-one there to hear his sad pleas for help. If only there had been a catflap in the kitchen door, he would have been home and dry hours ago, but humans always think they know best. He resigned himself to his fate and curled up on the carpet again, but the patch were he had lain had now gone cold. Some time later he heard the kitchen door open and a muffled voice call,

"Willi, come on, puss, puss, puss," as the cat meat saucer was tapped. He ran to the door of the shed and began miaowing for help, but the kitchen door closed again and that was that for the night.

It was still dark the following morning when he heard footsteps crunching through the snow. One of his humans was coming towards the shed, not to look for him but to find a shovel to clear the drive. It must have taken nearly five minutes to clear the snow from the door with the scoop the humans usually used to clear out Willi's litter tray. The human was very surprised to see Willi Whizkas!

"Why, there you are Willi, I called and called you but you never came, too lazy to move I suppose." Willi Whizkas was really pleased to see her as he was picked up and carried to the kitchen, as an extra-special treat he was given a whole tin of tuna flakes, which was almost worth being trapped in the shed for! As an extra privilege, he was allowed to stay in the house for the rest of the day, so to amuse himself he wandered from room to room looking out of the windows to examine the snow from every possible angle. Everywhere seemed so quiet with no cars moving, when the postman eventually came he was carrying his heavy bag as the snow was too deep for his bike. The children were let out of school early that afternoon and had a snowball fight which Willi Whizkas thought looked great fun. One horrible little boy saw him peeping out of the window and threw a snowball at him which landed on the window pane with a terrific thud! Willi Whizkas fled in terror and hid in the kitchen behind the pedal bin, wishing he was curled up on the duvet with Tushtots sharing some of his luxury scraps and telling tall tales of derring-do.

31 Santa Paws

As the days continued to be cold and dark, the east wind bought bitingly cold nights, his humans seemed to be spending more and more time at the shops, and lots of things were being put into cupboards and the freezer. Willi's cat food shelf was stacked high with tins of all different colours, although to his relief there wasn't a green one amongst them! The house was warm and cosy, Willi Whizkas felt strangely at peace with the world. On one of his rare excursions outside he explained what had been happening in his house to Tushtots.

"Do you know, it's rather odd you should say that," Tushtots told him, "the same sort of thing has been happening in my house. Lots of food, parcels being wrapped up in brightly coloured paper, of course I tried to help by sitting on the wrapping paper and chasing the string. That was fine until my claws burst through the last piece of wrapping paper, much to the annoyance of my humans. I'm not quite sure what it's all about but it does all look very important." They sought Gordon's advice.

"Oh yes, this sort of thing happens every year," Gordon told them knowledgeably when they were all inside sitting on Gordon's windowsill. "It's something the humans seem to do every year when the days are at their dullest and coldest, strange humans start singing on your doorstep at night and humans you haven't seen all year turn up to be fed at your house. But if you're lucky, boys, you'll get some extra-special treats, its a sort of indoor tree festival humans have at this time of year, – you'llsee soon enough" he laughed."

"I remember now," commented Tushtots, "It was at this strange time of year that I had my accident at my old house." Willi Whizkas narrowed his eyes and exhaled loudly "Hmmmph!!" Ginger Tompkins happened to be strolling by, so he popped into Gordon's house to see how everybody was.

"Here you all are," Ginger Tompkins greeted his chums, "found you all at last!" The parrot looked down from his cage with beady eyes and squawked "Gordon's been sick, Gordon's been sick," which attracted one of Gordon's humans, who rushed in from the dining room who was very surprised indeed to see four feline heads turn round and look at her.

"Goodness me, four of you," she exclaimed, "whatever shall we do with all you cats?" And she flicked a tea towel at them. The cats scarpered out of the catflap, Gordon bringing up the rear, limping. It was too cold to go anywhere or do anything so they all skulked off to their own homes.

Willi's humans had just come back from another shopping expedition, to his absolute astonishment there was a tree indoors! A bristly fir tree in a tub! The tree stood right in the middle of the lounge stretching all the way up to the ceiling, it must be the indoor tree festival that Gordon had mentioned.

"How very odd," thought Willi Whizkas to himself. He had often seen flowers in vases and plants in pots but the very idea of bringing a tree into the house seemed to be going that teeny-weeny bit too far. But then he remembered what Gordon had said about extra-special treats at this time of year, so he naturally thought that the tree was a gift for him from his humans.

"How very thoughtful," thought Willi Whizkas as he

sniffed at the lower branches and rubbed his face through the bristles. He suddenly found himself alone in the room. Now there was only one possible reason why the tree was there, it was obviously for him to use instead of having to go outside into the cold. Convinced that he was right, he backed up to it, all four paws together, lifted his tail and sprayed magnificently, a smile on his whiskers. His humans weren't so bad after all, this would make up for not having a cat flap.

He snoozed contentedly through the night, as the central heating had been left on he was as warm as toast. He had a rude awakening, however, when instead of going to work his humans came into the kitchen in dressing gowns and started to cook a delicious smelling breakfast. Willi Whizkas miaowed and purred and stretched up begging for bacon scraps, but instead of a tasty titbit he was dispatched to the garden.

"Hmmmph just my luck," Willi Whizkas grumped to himself, "they get me a tree to spray up but they won't share their bacon scraps with me. I'll never understand humans," and with that he decided to try his luck at Tushtots'. He found Tushtots tucking into a bowl of finely chopped bacon rinds, which had been cooked until they were golden brown and crispy. Willi Whizkas had smelt them halfway down the garden.

"Even a vegetarian cat would have to have some," drooled Willi Whizkas to himself. Tushtots kindly let him take one or two bacon scraps from his bowl, but then growled at him when he thought he was having too many, so Tushtots' human told him to share them nicely, then an unexpected bonus arrived in the form of a sausage which had fallen to the floor and got covered in hair and dust. Tushtots' humans seemed to be in a lazy, laid back frame of mind, both cats were encouraged to jump onto a lap for a stroke and to have their whiskers tickled. Willi

Whizkas wasn't a keen lap cat, but thought it was only fair having been given a welcome breakfast. He looked round and saw that Tushtots had been given a tree too, but it was much smaller than Willi's.

"That makes a pleasant change," Willi Whizkas thought smugly to himself, "it's unusual for me to have something better than the others."

With a glow of self satisfaction he nodded off and snoozed away until late afternoon, when he was put back outside in case his humans were looking for him.

When he got home he popped his head around the lounge door, then shrank back with amazement. His tree was now transformed into the most wondrous thing he had ever seen, covered in pretty coloured lights which twinkled on and off, with a little white star flashing right at the very top. Shiny strands of tinsel glittered and shone, small sacks of gold coins glinted, and underneath the tree there were lots and lots of parcels wrapped in bright paper and tied with pretty bows.

"Come on Christmas cat, come and have a look," his female human laughed, so he went up to the tree and sniffed. He could smell where he had sprayed that morning and was tempted to add to it, but thought better of it. Instead he sniffed the parcels one by one and his nose led him to a tiny package which smelt very interesting indeed. He put his paw on it, and was about to rip the paper off when he heard "No you don't you naughty cat, you can have that tomorrow and not before. We don't open our presents until Christmas Day."

He sat for what seemed ages spellbound by the twinkling lights and sparkling tinsel, more than once he was told off for trying to paw at the decorations.

On Christmas morning Willi Whizkas was woken from a deep sleep by the oven timer kicking into action, within half an hour the delicious aroma of roasting meat filled the kitchen. Soon the humans got up, and made the first cup of tea of the day.

"Morning Willi, happy Christmas!" Willi Whizkas wasn't sure what all that meant but he appreciated having his back scratched and his ears squeezed.

Willi Whizkas' tummy grumbled and rumbled as the turkey cooked, but he was distracted by his humans beckoning him to join them in the lounge for present opening. The parcels were taken from under the tree, the wrappings torn off to sounds of 'ohhhs aaaahhhs' and 'thank yous' and the humans exchanged kisses. Willi Whizkas sniffed at each new item as it was unwrapped, but it wasn't so much the presents that interested him as the wrapping paper. He lunged headlong into several pieces tearing at them with his claws, and tried to hide under the bigger sheets. Best of all was one of the boxes which was just big enough for him to pour himself into and then peep over the top.

"Come on Willi, it's your turn," came an invitation, and Willi Whizkas was given a small thin parcel which he sniffed and pawed at a couple of times as a human unwrapped it for him. He couldn't believe his eyes when his Christmas treat for being a good cat all year turned out to be a bright yellow collar with a small cissy bell!! His heart sank as he hated collars and sissy bells, they marked him out as a 'kept' cat, instead of the 'rough-tough-go-get-em' type he always considered himself to be.

"One more present Willi Whizkas, we don't want to spoil you too much, but this is your favourite!"

As soon as he sniffed the offered package, his eyes began to glaze over, and he frantically ripped the paper to shreds to reveal a catnip mouse, not one of the cheap ones either, but a very special one which had been ordered on the Internet from the CATNIP TOY CO of

Felix Arizona. He spent a good half an hour drooling into his new mouse as he rolled round the carpet with it. He chewed it, bit it, sniffed it, rolled on it and eventually lay on his back with his legs in the air in a state of total bliss. Meanwhile in the kitchen the female human pulled the turkey sizzling from the oven, she pronounced it well and truly cooked. Willi Whizkas couldn't wait, he just had to have some at any price and he jumped onto the work surface right next to where the turkey was cooling down. He got within a whisker of the crisp golden skin, when he was unceremoniously dumped on the floor.

"Oh no you don't my laddeo," snapped his female human, "you'll get your share all in good time." Eventually the meat was carved, the wine was poured and the humans sat down to dine. Still nothing came Willi's way until, mewing pitifully, he was handed a tender piece of warm turkey. Never had anything ever tasted quite so good so he mewed again and again until he got another piece. But he was so hungry he couldn't control himself, and stretched up to his full height until his nose almost reached the table top. He reached up with a paw and patted around on the table cloth in the hope of catching a piece of turkey.

"Down Willi, you naughty cat, you'll get some scraps when I strip the carcass," shouted his female human, and just to keep him quiet she gave him another piece of turkey. Later, as promised, he was given a generous mound of off-cuts and trimmings with some lovely crisp turkey skin. He wasn't too sure about the stuffing though, cats don't really do stuffing. He ate and ate and ate until he felt like he would burst, then he burped and threatened to bring the lot back up again, but he swallowed deeply and all was well!

A good ten minutes of paw and whisker washing followed, then Willi Whizkas just managed to squeeze himself and his stuffed tummy into his new cardboard box, where he curled up and went to sleep. The humans dozed the afternoon away as well, but did wake up in time for the Queen's speech, although by the time the big film had started they were fast asleep again. Shortly before dark, the male human remembered that there was one last present for Willi Whizkas, so he lifted him gently from the box and, cradling him upside down in his arms, whispered gently "Wake up Willi, come and see what Santa Paws has brought for you," with that he carried him outside and showed him something that he'd always wanted. Willi' sleepy eyes widened in surprise, because there in all it's shiny new glory was his very own catflap!!!

32 Timber!!

On Boxing Day Willi Whizkas got some choice scraps of turkey for breakfast instead of the usual tinned cat meat. The turkey was colder than he would have liked, having been in the fridge, but still tasted good. He ate as much as he could, then set off to try out his new catflap, putting his head through it a few times going in and out repeatedly until he was fully satisfied with it. He glowed with pride as he swaggered off down the garden in search of his playmates, but not before he had done a round of his garden, sniffing at every bush, spraying on one for good measure. Then he looked under the shed on the off-chance that a family of mice might have set up home there. He sniffed deeply at the shed, but could only detect a faint smell of Ginger Tompkins, who was in the habit of coming into his garden and spraying. Willi Whizkas didn't mind because he could return the compliment up the side of Ginger Tompkins' wheelie-bin, and that was where Willi Whizkas was heading. The cold weather made him want to spray more than usual.

Willi Whizkas was surprised in mid-spray by the appearance of Ginger Tompkins, and what an appearance! Ginger Tompkins was wearing the brightest red collar imaginable, with a little tinkly bell which sounded remarkably like the one round Willi Whizkas's neck!

"Well, our humans will know where we are now, won't they old chap?" Ginger Tompkins laughed, his bell tinkling as he chuckled.

"I'm hoping I'll have lost mine by baby bird season," sniggered Willi Whizkas cheerfully, "I'll never catch one with this thing jangling round my neck!" He was a past-master at losing collars, having already lost several, so he promised Ginger Tompkins he would show him how it was done.

"Let's go and see what Tushtots got for Christmas, I bet he's been spoilt rotten," suggested Willi Whizkas enviously, "he always seems to get the best of everything."

"Well, old thing you must admit that he is generous, so no matter what he's had we'll all benefit," argued Ginger Tompkins.

"That's true," agreed Willi Whizkas, they were just cutting across to Tushtots' when they heard a third bell jingling.

"It can't be," Willi Whizkas gasped.

"It certainly sounds like it could be, old chap," Ginger Tompkins observed, it was true. But it wasn't Tushtots it was Britney Kitney, who was wearing a new collar. Her's was bright pink and had an equally ridiculous tinkly bell dangling from it.

"Not you as well?" Willi Whizkas chuckled,

"'Fraid so," confirmed Britney Kitney, "but you have to look pleased for the humans don't you?"

Britney Kitney had started to go on one or two small adventures with the toms, who hadn't been sure at first, but she seemed a good sort and was easily impressed with the tall tales and high jinx of the intrepid trio. However her closest friendship seemed to be with Gordon, but they suspected that it was only so that she could go into his house and see his bird in the cage. Willi Whizkas and Ginger Tompkins squeezed through Tushtots' catflap into his kitchen.

"Hello you two, happy Christmas!" Tushtots's male

human greeted them, "it looks like great minds have thought alike in the cat present department!" He bent down to give the toms a stroke from their whiskers right down to the tips of their tails.

"Your little pal is in the lounge sleeping off an excess of turkey, go and see him if you like." Willi Whizkas nosed the lounge door open, Ginger Tompkins followed him. Tushtots opened a bleary eye and let out a small snigger.

"Well that makes three of us," he said, stretching his neck to reveal a bright blue collar.

"Better make that four," chuckled Ginger Tompkins, explaining that they had just bumped into Britney Kitney who was sporting a bright pink collar.

"Well I'm blessed!" Tushtots exclaimed, "they must have had a run on them in the pet shop!!"

"Did you get any other presents?" Willi Whizkas enquired, hoping it would be something edible.

"Oh yes," confirmed Tushtots, "I've got the most marvellous contraption!"

"Have you? Are you going to show us?" Willi suggested.

"Certainly," Tushtots told them, "allow me to demonstrate." He jumped down from the sofa then padded across the lounge, leading the boys to a a beautiful sheepskin hammock hanging from the radiator, where a cat could doze for hours in perfect warmth, comfort and luxury.

"What do you think of it then lads?" Tushtots asked.

"It looks fantastic old thing," enthused Ginger Tompkins.

"Come on Tushtots, give us a go," pleaded Willi Whizkas and he jumped into it the very second that Tushtots jumped out. It was truly fabulous!!

"Mmmm, not sure it's the thing for me," sniffed Willi Whizkas snootily, "I think I'd get a little too warm."

"Oh, I don't think so," purred Ginger Tompkins, "on a cold night I could make use of one of these."

"Is that it?" Willi Whizkas yawned rudely, "anything else?"

"No, That's about it," said Tushtots, "apart from lots of succulent turkey of course, but what was even tastier was one of those sausages wrapped in bacon that had been cooked next to the turkey." Willi Whizkas drooled at the thought of it.

"Don't suppose you've got one left have you?"

"'Fraid not, I only got the one and I ate the lot."

"I got a basket," Ginger Tompkins butted in as he hopped out of the hammock, "it doesn't clip onto the radiator though. It's got a hole at one end and you climb into it, it's quite dark when you get inside but there's a nice soft cushion to curl up on. I think it's home-made, but there's nothing wrong with home-made presents it they fit the job."

"So Wills, what did you get apart from that rather flash collar?" Tushtots asked. Willi Whizkas was about to explain, but deciding to show them instead, led the way back to his own garden.

"Here it is, what do you think of that?" Willi Whizkas invited a response as he pointed to his present with his claw. Tushtots and Ginger Tompkins jaws dropped, their eyes widened, as they stared in disbelief. It was Willi's pride and joy, his very own catflap. Tushtots and Ginger couldn't stop themselves from bursting into laughter as Willi Whizkas became very cross. He had waited all his life for a catflap, and now the moment was being spoiled by his best friends.

"Well I think it's wonderful," Willi Whizkas snorted.

"Yes," agreed Tushtots, "but it doesn't actually go into your house, it only goes into your garden shed!!" Willi's eyes narrowed and he stamped a paw furiously, but he wasn't going to let them get the better of him.

"Come inside and take a closer look," instructed Willi Whizkas as he thrust his nose into the air and strutted in a superior fashion through the catflap. Tushtots and Ginger Tompkins followed Willi Whizkas into his shed, it was only when they were inside that they realised just what Willi Whizkas had been given for Christmas. The old bikes, cobwebs, garden tools and bits of carpet had all gone, and the inside of the shed had been given a designer makeover. The windows had been cleaned, there was a ledge covered in warm carpet with a ladder leading up to it, which Willi Whizkas proceeded to climb.

"Perfect view over the garden," boasted Willi Whizkas, "I can see my house, the pond, I can see over to your house Tushtots, and I can keep my eye on any birds or mice that come onto my patch."

On the back wall was a large wicker basket, raised off the floor lined with a soft plump pillow. Hanging from the middle of the roof was a ping-pong ball covered in feathers, which he could pat back and forth. But best of all was the new-fangled device which allowed cat biscuits to roll out of the bottom, as Willi Whizkas ate them more dropped down to take their place. Ginger Tompkins and Tushtots looked on in amazement.

"It's your very own palace Willi Whizkas," breathed Tushtots in admiration.

"You can come and go as you like old chap," said Ginger Tompkins, "anytime of the day or night."

"I think I'm going to spend many a night in here," laughed Willi Whizkas excitedly.

"We could all come!" Tushtots suggested.

"Of course you can," invited Willi Whizkas, "we could use it as a clubhouse to plan our adventures."

The kitchen door to Willi's real house opened, as his human called him in.

"That's it," Willi Whizkas said to the other two, "I'm off inside, it's time for a bite to eat."

"More turkey, probably," groaned Tushtots. Willi Whizkas wasn't too sure how to take the comment, he'd enjoyed every mouthful he had ever been given! When he got inside, the door was smartly closed behind him.

"Got you Willi, come and see who wants to see you," Willi Whizkas stopped dead in his tracks, confronted by a whole roomful of humans!

"Come on Willi, come and meet the family," his female human ordered. He had met them before, but never all together like this, so he wasn't sure what to do.

"My how you've grown," commented Great Aunt Beryl as she bent to pick him up. Willi Whizkas wriggled his way free, walked over uncle Wally's knee, then jumped on to the back of the sofa.

"Come off there Willi, go and see Grandma, she likes cats." Grandma patted her lap and beckoned, she was a kindly old lady who smelt like a lavender bush, but Willi was really more interested in food, in particular a large plate of sandwiches which he had just spotted. They were mostly turkey, but there were a few salmon sandwiches too, salmon being a favourite of Willi Whizkas'. He especially liked the black skin, which for some reason the humans didn't eat, so he spent the next half hour shamelessly begging for titbits. When all the sandwiches had been polished off he sat in front of the fire, raised his back right leg as far as it would go, then began to wash his bottom.

"Now there's a sight for you, and you let cats lick your face!" Grandpa pointed out as he threw a slipper in Willi's direction, which brought the cat cabaret to an abrupt end.

Willi Whizkas went round the back of the Christmas tree and, as he was hidden from view, everyone forgot that he was there. He looked up and noticed that there were some sturdy branches which he thought were strong enough to take his weight, so very carefully he started to climb, taking care not to disturb the decorations at the front of the tree. He had plenty of bush climbing practice when he was out stalking birds, but as yet, there was no sign of a nest in this particular tree. The higher he went the more the tree started to sway from side to side, but nobody noticed as they were all preoccupied with Great Aunt Beryl who was choking on a coconut macaroon!

Willi Whizkas reached the twinkling star just as Great Aunt Beryl was laid out full length on the sofa, at which point Willi Whizkas lost his balance, which caused the tree to lose it's balance. In what seemed like slow motion Willi's Christmas tree, the flashing star, the twinkling lights and the glinting tinsel slowly toppled into the crowded room. Grandma screamed, Grandpa yelled "Timber!!", then everyone gasped as Willi Whizkas landed awkwardly in a half-eaten dish of trifle spraying custard in all directions. Grandpa just looked at him and whispered "You've got your just desserts my lad!!"

33 False alarm

It was a miserable wet Saturday and Willi Whizkas couldn't be bothered to go outside, so he was watching rain drops run down the window pane. He'd focus on one high up on the glass and watch it snake its way down to the bottom getting bigger and bigger, but, try as he might, he couldn't see one start its journey. The more he looked the more puzzled he became, so he gave it up as a bad job. His humans were sitting around reading the newspapers, taking it in turns to read snippets to each other.

"Five down, a cat that could be found on a golf course . . . something, something something . . . Oh, lynx."

After lunch the rain stopped, so Willi Whizkas went outside to do his business and find his pals. He popped into his palace where he discovered Ginger Tompkins and Tushtots taking full advantage of his window seat and, much to Willi's annoyance, the last of his crunch cat biscuits.

"There you are, we were just about to give up on you for the day," said Tushtots with his mouth full.

"Well, it wasn't really nice enough to come out until now," replied Willi Whizkas.

"Poor excuse old chap, " retorted Ginger Tompkins, "Tushtots and I have been in here hours waiting for you."

"Why, has something important happened?" Willi Whizkas asked.

"Could be," Ginger Tompkins told him "we've had a summons."

"A summons, what do you mean a summons?"

"I saw Gordon late yesterday, he tells me that Thugsby wants to see us, old thing."

"Thugsby? What on earth can he want?" Willi Whizkas asked, "we haven't seen him for weeks."

"I'm not sure, but it's best to do as he says, he was a bit of a mean character in his alley cat days. I wouldn't want to cross paws with him, old chap," Ginger Tompkins pointed out.

The weather was still fine as they made a dash across the wet lawn, down the drive, under the gate and across the road to Gordon's house. Gordon was sitting watching the world go by, taking a breath of fresh air having been cooped up all day.

"What's happening Gordon?" Willi Whizkas pleaded, "what's this about Thugsby wanting to see us?"

"I'm not sure," replied Gordon, " he just said he wanted to see the three of you urgently."

"Not you Gordon?" Willi Whizkas enquired further.

"Nope . . . just you three."

"Oh dear, I hope we're not in some sort of trouble," sighed Tushtots.

"I wouldn't have thought so," said Gordon thoughtfully, "he's been a reformed character for a while, he probably just wants a bit of muscle to sort out a problem he might have."

"That sounds like fun old fruit," smiled Ginger Tompkins.

"I don't know," Tushtots added nervously, "I don't really like fighting!"

"Nonsense!" Willi Whizkas exploded, "all cats like a good scrap. I haven't met a cat yet who didn't, anyway, you'll be all right Tushtots. We'd better go and find him then."

"Don't forget to let me know what it's all about," Gordon called after them as they set off for Thugsby's adopted home. Thugsby was upstairs in a bedroom window, and spotted them well before they arrived. He slithered out onto the windowsill, leapt athletically onto the garage roof, shinned down a water-butt and was on the patio in no time.

"Goodness me you make that look easy!" Willi Whizkas gasped.

"Did I?" Thugsby asked, "Years of practice getting in and out of houses, second nature to a cat from my background!"

"You wouldn't need a catflap if you could do that, Willi old chap," laughed Ginger Tompkins.

"You know, I think your right," Willi replied. "Come to think of it I did escape from the little girl's house once, but the jump down from the garage made my paws sore for days!"

"Well, I'm glad you came lads," Thugsby said.

"Why's that?" Tushtots asked timidly, "is there going to be a fight or anything?"

"Fighting? Goodness me no, "laughed Thugsby, "who on earth told you that?" The name Gordon was on Tushtots's lips, but Willi Whizkas interrupted.

"What was it that you had in mind, Thugsby?"

"I'll show you. Look up there, the small bedroom window on the right. Tell me what you see.?"

The bewildered threesome stared and puzzled, the more they stared the more puzzled they became.

"What are we supposed to see?" Tushtots asked, "I can only see curtains."

"Wait a minute old chap," said Ginger Tompkins, " I think I can see something going round and round."

"Exactly!!" Thugsby exclaimed, "Now, what you lads might not be able to see from here but I can see from my upstairs window is two very fat hamsters in a cage, and what you can see going round and round is their exercise wheel!"

"Do you know, I do believe I can see them old fruit," confirmed Ginger Tompkins.

"So, what's the deal then Thuggers?" Willi Whizkas asked.

"Simple," replied Thugsby, "we need to get inside, then I need your muscle to help me knock the cage open and hopefully spring the hamsters free. Then it's yum yum hamster for supper! There's some nice eating on a hamster, once you get through the fur!"

"But surely that's breaking and entering?" Tushtots observed.

"That's right lad, we break into the cage so that the hamsters can enter our tummies!" Thugsby chuckled.

"So how do we get in without being seen, old bean?" Ginger Tompkins enquired.

"Easy," replied Thugsby, "the humans go out to bingo every Saturday night, and the kids are at their granny's so there'll be nobody there at all tonight." They sat on the wall for a while, watched the house, after a good deal of staring Willi Whizkas could make out the exercise wheel going round and round.

"How big is a hamster Mr Thugsby?" Tushtots enquired.

"Well, It's nearly the size of a good rat, but much more succulent!"

It started to spit with rain so they all ran to the back of Thugsby's house to shelter by the side of the old coal bunker.

"I'm not sure about how we are going to get in," mused a worried Tushtots.

"That's easy," Thugsby told him, "you saw how I got out of my house this afternoon? Well it's the same, but in reverse." This revelation hardly filled the mouseketeers with confidence, but time soon passed and the appointed hour arrived.

"That sounds like the car leaving now," observed Thugsby. "Come on lads, let's take a look." A shiny new car reversed out, then sped away down the road.

"Right, this is it, we're going in!" Thugsby ordered, they darted across the road and up their victim's drive. Thugsby stopped to see that the coast was clear.

"OK lads, here we go." Thugsby made it all look so easy, it took him no time at all to bound onto the sill and through the window next to the hamster's room. Ginger Tompkins was next, if Thugsby could do it then he could do it, and anyway youth was on his side.

"Don't let me go last," pleaded Tushtots.

"Come on," Willi Whizkas egged him on, "I'll follow you and make sure you'll be all right."

"I'm frightened," whispered Tushtots, "I might fall off and hurt myself!"

"Nonsense," snapped Willi Whizkas as he pushed past Tushtots and sprang onto the windowsill. " See, there's nothing to it."

"I think I'll stay here," Tushtots called up to him, "I know I can't make it!"

"OK. Stand guard on the roof then," instructed Willi Whizkas, "if anyone comes, give us a yowl." Tushtots timidly agreed. However the cat's plans hadn't quite gone as smoothly as they should. The hamsters were in the room next to the one they had entered, and the door to the hamsters' room was closed,3 no amount of pushing or scratching would open it.

"Stand clear!" Thugsby ordered, "I've got an idea." He sprang up to the door handle, curled his paws around it and used his weight to pull the handle down, causing the door to open.

"Come on," whispered Thugsby, "we're in." Three pairs of eyes now stared in through the bars of the cage, where one of the hamsters was sitting on his back legs, paws raised, washing his whiskers while the other, even plumper, was running round and round on the exercise wheel. They didn't see the cats at first, but soon got the message when Willi's jaws began to chatter.

"There we are lads, that's supper!" Thugsby announced proudly. With a good deal of effort they managed to push the cage over, the door did indeed spring open as Thugsby had planned. Simultaneously, Thugsby and Willi Whizkas lunged at the open door but ended up banging their heads together, causing sufficient confusion for the hamsters to make a run for it.

"Quick! After them!" Ginger Tompkins called, the cats set off in hot pursuit. The hamsters made straight for the open door and shot down the stairs as fast as their tiny legs would let them. At this point the burglar alarm, being sufficiently sensitive to be triggered by three cats moving as one, began to wail it's extremely loud warning throughout the house, and indeed across the avenue. The terrible trio froze.

"What on earth is all that racket?" Willi Whizkas shouted.

"It's a burglar alarm," Thugsby informed him, "Quick, scarper," but the wind had blown the bedroom door firmly shut and there was no way out. They were completely trapped.

Two police cars and the dog van arrived just minutes later, and the cats could hear Sergeant Fang barking his authority. A loud hammering at the front door started, torches were shone through the letter box, while Sergeant Fang barked ever more ferociously.

"Round the back," commanded a policeman and a constable plodded round to the back of the house.

"No sign of anyone here, Sarge," he reported.

"Right lads, look lively," instructed Thugsby, "we have to make this look like a false alarm!"

"How can we do that?" Asked Willi Whizkas nervously.

"Well, There's nothing to indicate that we don't actually live here," smirked Thugsby, "just act natural-like. Willi Whizkas, you go and sit in the window, Gingie, you curl up on the sofa, I'll stretch out on the television." Moments later three policemen and a snarling Fang burst through into the house and switched all the lights on, but alas for the young constable who had entered from the rear, in the confusion Fang mistook him for a burglar and gave him a nasty bite on the bottom. "Ambulance, ambulance, get me an ambulance!" He screamed in pain.

Once immediate assistance and reinforcements had been requested, the officers finally entered the lounge. Ginger Tompkins climbed the curtains and Thugsby jumped onto a bookshelf, which left a very, very frightened Willi Whizkas staring Sergeant Fang in the eye, desperately hoping that the fearsome dog had forgotten all about the time when Willi Whizkas had sprayed on him through the bars of his kennel. Unfortunately he clearly did remember, but the dog was restrained by his handler just in time before his snapping jaws could exact revenge on Willi Whizkas. By the time the police had finished their search of the premises the owners had arrived back from their bingo session. The police explained what had happened, adding that there was no sign of a forced entry, and that their cats were safe and well.

"Cats? But we haven't got a cat!!!

"You have sir, you've got three." However, the cats

had made a quick exit and regrouped in Thugsby's back garden.

"I thought I'd seen the last of you three when I saw Sergeant Fang!" Tushtots whimpered.

"No," bragged Willi Whizkas, "it was just a false alarm!"

34 A Thorny Problem

Although Willi's shed catflap was a bit of a disappointment to start with, he had soon realised it was quite a useful thing to have, and had taken full advantage. It had kept him warm and dry on bad days, it was somewhere he could lie low and lick his wounds if he'd had a fight, but most of all it had been useful as a meeting place for himself, Ginger Tompkins, Tushtots and, more recently, Britney Kitney. The only downside of Willi's little kingdom was his cat biscuits disappearing at an alarming rate. This was a thorny little problem, with this firmly in mind he sat in the sunshine one morning and worked out a plan of action. He needed to watch who came and went from his garden, and, more importantly, which cats were going into his palace stealing the biscuits. Should he make himself a little hide that he could peep out from without being noticed, or just keep an eye out from the kitchen window which overlooked the garden and the catflap? He thought no more of it for a day or two until he caught sight of Tushtots making a beeline for his catflap. Willi Whizkas stared from the kitchen window in disbelief, was Tushtots the thief?

Willi Whizkas miaowed at the kitchen door to go out, then slithered across the garden on his tummy as quietly as he could. He gently nosed the catflap open just enough to see inside. There, as large as life was Tushtots, crunching his way through the biscuits. Willi Whizkas didn't say anything, he just watched, unable to believe just how many biscuits Tushtots was eating. When

Tushtots had had his fill, Willi Whizkas pushed his way into his palace and greeted Tushtots as if he hadn't seen anything.

"Oh, there you are Willi Whizkas," greeted Tushtots, "I'd come to look for you."

"Have you been here long?" Willi Whizkas asked.

"Oh no, I've only just arrived," lied Tushtots.

Over the next few days Willi Whizkas kept up his surveillance, the only cat that he ever saw going through the catflap was Tushtots. Now Willi Whizkas had often eaten tasty scraps at Tushtots's house, but they had always been offered, he'd never helped himself. Willi's selective memory appeared to have completely forgotten that he himself had been just as big a thief by helping himself to Gordon's leftovers.

It was now spring, which opened up all sorts of opportunities for mischievous cats, such as butterfly hunting. There was an old lady in the next street who had the most magnificent buddleia bush, which attracted butterflies like an unburied cat poo attracts flies! The bush was covered in dozens of beautiful purple flower spikes, which in turn were covered in dazzling butterflies with big eyes painted on their wings. The cats watched spellbound as the butterflies fluttered from flower to flower probing for nectar. Willi Whizkas made one of his famous athletic leaps high into the air, but missed the butterflies by a mile and crashed helplessly onto a patch of nettles. Now nettles don't normally bother a cat but Willi Whizkas had been very unlucky, and got a nasty sting on the tender part of his nostril, so he let out a pained yowl and rubbed his nose with his paw.

"What have you done, Willi Whizkas?" Britney Kitney enquired, all concerned.

"I've stung my nose, that's what I've done." He snapped back.

"Come here, let's take a look." Britney Kitney examined Willi's nose very carefully, but all she could see was a small crusty bogey.

"I can't see anything," she told him.

"Well I've definitely stung myself," he insisted, but while he was playing the wounded martyr Ginger Tompkins was more successful, having managed to catch one of the butterflies and send it spinning into the long grass. Every time it tried to flutter away Ginger Tompkins would put out his paw then bring it back down to earth again, but Britney Kitney saw what he was doing and thought he was being needlessly cruel.

"I thought the idea was to eat them," she called out, "not play with them."

"Oh no," replied Ginger Tompkins, "The fun is in the tormenting."

Tushtots agreed, which is why of course some animals 'play dead' when cornered by a cat, who then loses interest in it when it doesn't move. They all played in the sunshine chasing the butterflies until something else caught their attention. A patch of thistles had just begun to release their seeds on little feathery parachutes, which floated on the lightest of breezes like skeletons of stars. The cats sat and watched them, entranced. The more the breeze blew the more of these wondrous, lighter than air, floaty things passed over their heads, so the butterflies were given a bit of peace as the cats tried their paw at catching the seedlings. It was great fun, especially when Willi Whizkas made yet another of his crash landings, only this time again he wasn't so lucky! He landed with his front paw on a very nasty, very prickly bramble, and one of the thorns pierced one of his soft pink pads. This time it was serious, the thorn had broken off and was embedded deep in his paw, blood was beginning to appear, which he licked at but that just made it hurt even more. The rest of the gang gathered round to see what he had done.

"That's looks nasty." Tushtots stated the obvious.

"I've seen worse though," said Ginger Tompkins reassuringly.

"Well, I haven't," added Britney Kitney, "what's going to happen now Willi?" Willi Whizkas thought he knew the answer to that and he was right: It was the limp that gave him away when he eventually turned up for his supper. His humans were not best pleased, they'd lost count of the number of times Willi had been to the vet.

"That vet always welcomes us with an open till," grumbled his male human. The thorn was removed with a large pair of forceps and he was given an injection in his neck by a nurse, after which his paw was lovingly bandaged. His humans were given instructions to keep his paw dry for at least a week, which meant no adventures. Willi Whizkas was confined to the house, which was going to prove an interesting period in his life. After a couple of days he was feeling well enough to jump onto the kitchen draining board and sit beside the window to survey the comings and goings in his garden. This was going to be a special opportunity for him to continue his watch on his little palace to see who came and went, and more importantly, who was stealing his biscuits. Ginger Tompkins was the first to come into his garden, sniffing around the bushes and spraying all Willi Whizkas' favourite spots before going through the catflap into the palace.

"Ah ha!" Thought Willi Whizkas. Perhaps Ginger Tompkins was also stealing his biscuits, but Ginger Tompkins could see that Willi Whizkas wasn't in the palace, so he came back out then wandered off into the afternoon. Now it was looking more and more as if Tushtots was the sole phantom biscuit snaffler, especially when at no time during Willi's confinement did Britney Kitney stray into his garden. Tushtots was by far the most frequent visitor, slinking into the garden whenever he thought the coast was clear, then sneaking into the palace where he would stay for several long minutes before re-emerging, licking his lips. There was no doubt in Willi's mind, Tushtots was the thief, there would have to be words. As soon as Willi was passed fit again the first thing he did was to go to his palace, where he discovered his biscuits were all gone, every last one! Tushtots had scoffed the lot. Fired up with anger, he strutted across to Tushtots' garden to have it out with him. Tushtots tried to plead innocence, but Willi Whizkas was having none of it, and informed the robber cat of his observations while wounded. It was no use denying it, Tushtots had been caught out fair and square, but Willi's temper was now running away with him. In a fit of rage he told Tushtots not to bother to come into his garden, or his palace ever again. As far as he was concerned, Tushtots was no longer welcome to join in with the gang's adventures. Tushtots' eyes welled up with tears, after all the generosity he had shown Willi Whizkas this is how he was being repaid. He had thought that Willi Whizkas would have been pleased to share his treats, especially as Willi's biscuits were so much nicer than the ones Tushtots got at his home.

As a parting gesture, Willi Whizkas reared up and gave Tushtots a nasty bite on the neck before storming back to his own garden with his head and tail firmly in the air, convinced that he was right. He settled down on the comfy cushion in his palace and tried to get some sleep, but his mind kept thinking of the events of the last few minutes. Had he been too severe with Tushtots? Was he right to exclude him from adventures with himself, Ginger Tompkins and Britney Kitney? But the more he thought about it the more he struggled to come to the right decision and sleep only came after a lot of soul-searching. He was eventually woken when one of his humans undid the door to his palace to refill the biscuit dispenser.

"Goodness me, Willi Whizkas, have you eaten all those? You are getting a greedy cat," bending down to give him a little stroke and a tickle under his chin, but Willi's mood still wasn't settled and he bit the hand that fed him!!

"Willi Whizkas! You naughty cat, what ever's got into you?" A long finger was wagged in his direction, so he let out a warning hiss.

"You're getting to be a really bad cat Willi, you can come into the house when your temper's improved." Later that evening, whilst he was still ensconced in his palace, the catflap creaked and a head poked its cautious way inside. It was Ginger Tompkins.

"There you are Willi old fruit," he said as he pulled himself through, followed by Britney Kitney. The two of them sat down and glared at Willi Whizkas.

"Now, what's all this about then Willi?" Ginger Tompkins demanded.

"All what?" Asked Willi Whizkas innocently with a bored yawn.

"You know, upsetting Tushtots and accusing him of biscuit snaffling," snapped Ginger Tompkins.

"Well," replied Willi Whizkas, "I've a right to, he's been in and out of my palace all week whilst I've been recuperating, and he's eaten all my biscuits without being invited."

"That's no reason to set about him, old fruit." insisted Ginger Tompkins.

"I agree," piped up Britney Kitney, "I think you're being very mean Willi." Willi Whizkas was now more convinced than ever that he was right.

"And another thing," Ginger Tompkins went on, "what's all this about Tushtots not being allowed to join in our adventures? Who are you to make that sort of decision? I don't recall you being elected gang leader or anything." It was true, he hadn't, he had just naturally assumed that he was in charge. Ginger Tompkins then went on to remind Willi Whizkas that he'd done very well indeed out of his friendship with Tushtots, who'd always shown good hospitality, giving Willi warmth and shelter when his humans had thrown him outside on cold wet days. Willi Whizkas thought about all this for a few moments and eventually accepted Ginger Tompkins point of view.

"I suppose you're right, I've been too quick to condemn Tushtots," Willi Whizkas mumbled.

"I think that you owe Tushtots a big apology," insisted Ginger Tompkins, "and there's no time like the present!" Britney Kitney agreed and off they went to find Tushtots, but Tushtots was nowhere to be found and his catflap was firmly locked shut. By now Willi Whizkas was very ashamed of what he'd done, and was desperate to say sorry.

35 *The Final Farewell.*

Willi Whizkas felt really miserable, he'd intended to make friends with Tushtots after the quarrel that they'd had over the biscuits, but Tushtots was nowhere to be seen. Tushtots hadn't made any attempt to come and find Willi Whizkas either, so this looked like a serious rift in their friendship. Willi Whizkas went round to see if Ginger Tompkins had any news.

"'Fraid not old boy," Ginger Tompkins told him, "I've seen neither hide nor hair of him." Britney Kitney hadn't seen Tushtots either, it was no good asking Archibald the rabbit, he just sat looking stupid and twitching his large nose, but Willi Whizkas wouldn't have asked the rabbit anyway, he gave Archibald a wide berth these days. He sauntered gloomily across the road to Gordon's house, just as a small white van pulled up. He took no notice of it as he pushed his way into Gordon's kitchen, feeling so depressed he didn't even bother to inspect Gordon's leftovers.

Gordon was in the pantry trying to catch what must have been the world's largest house spider which had scuttled behind the gas meter when Gordon attempted to pounce on it. Even the prospect of an enormous spider didn't lift Willi's gloom. After a few minutes Gordon gave up staring at the gas meter.

"I'll catch that spider later," he grumped, "I've nearly caught it a couple of times, but it's just that little bit too quick for my old bones." Willi Whizkas thought how lucky Gordon was to have a pantry with spiders, newer houses like Willi's just had a load of cupboards, which weren't nearly as much fun. Willi Whizkas went into the lounge following Gordon, who jumped up into the window then sat in his favourite spot surveying the street.

"Oh look!" gasped Gordon with a strange tone in his voice.

"What?"

"Look!" Gordon Instructed, "there's a strange human in your garden, he's hammering a post into the ground with a big yellow sign on it! I bet you don't know what that is?" Gordon quizzed.

"I've absolutely no idea," Willi Whizkas had to admit.

"Well, I think I know," mused Gordon thoughtfully, "there was one in the front garden of the family that moved out just before the little girl's family moved in."

"And....?" Willi Whizkas failed to make the connection.

"I think it means that your humans are leaving your house."

"But that's impossible!" Willi Whizkas scoffed, "where would they go, they only have one house?"

"I think humans do a swap or something when they get fed up," Gordon told him knowledgeably. Willi Whizkas was now quite worried, he turned and gave the new sign in the garden a very hard stare hoping that Gordon was wrong. Ginger Tompkins wasn't long in paying Willi Whizkas a visit, he'd see the sign go up too, and came up with more or less the same story that Gordon had told him. Willi Whizkas made him promise that he hadn't made this story up with Gordon to tease him.

"The next thing you'll know old fruit," Ginger Tompkins told him, "is one of those huge removal vans will come."

"But what about me?" Wailed Willi Whizkas, "what's going to happen to me?"

"Well Willi, you've got precisely two choices, you can move away with your humans to a new house, or you can make yourself scarce and avoid moving with them." Willi Whizkas liked the sound of the second choice, but then realised the consequences.

"Who's going to feed me? The biscuits don't get into my palace by magic!"

"No," replied Ginger Tompkins, "they don't."

"I could always go and live at Tushtots' house, he's always keen to share his food!" Willi Whizkas suggested, before remembering that he had fallen out with Tushtots, and that he was very unlikely to be invited into Tushtots' house ever again. This made him even more miserable, and more determined than ever to make up with Tushtots.

Days passed with no sign of Tushtots anywhere, and no sign of the removal van either. Willi Whizkas became convinced that Gordon and Ginger Tompkins were wrong, but just in case, he thought he'd better have one of his plans at the ready. Perhaps the little girl would take him in? He ambled over to see Gordon, who deemed it a fine plan, he suggested Willi Whizkas spend more time with the little girl, and make his peace with Archibald the rabbit.

"That's what I'll do then," enthused Willi Whizkas, he went straight over to the little girl's house to present himself for adoption. He talked it over with Britney Kitney, who was over the moon with the idea, she quite liked Willi Whizkas' scatterbrained master plans and schemes, and she'd enjoyed being tucked up in the pram with Willi Whizkas and taken for 'baby-walks'.

"We could do some more of that if you came to live with us forever," smiled Britney Kitney, Willi Whizkas agreed. When the little girl came out of school, Willi Whizkas began to make a fuss, a lot of fuss of her. He rubbed his tail round her legs and when she tried to stroke him he stretched up on his hind legs and nuzzled her face, his little damp nose brushing her cheek like a kiss.

"Ahh, Willi Whizkas you big softy, you've given me a kiss," she picked him up and, cradling him in her arms, kissed him back. Being cute and appealing was obviously working.

He followed her into the house and tried to make himself at home, curling up in an easy chair as if he owned the place. Whilst the little girl's mother was delighted to see Willi Whizkas she wasn't too pleased to see his dirty paws on her furniture, so she scooped him up, opened the kitchen door and put him outside.

"You can come back when you're clean," she told him. He plodded dejectedly into the garden and jumped on top of the rabbit hutch, feeling his master plan had gone all wrong right from the start. To cheer himself up, Willi Whizkas started poking his paw through the wire just to annoy Archibald, but the little girl's mother saw him, and banged angrily on the kitchen window before running out clapping her hands to shoo him away.

"Things aren't going to well," muttered Britney Kitney to herself, "it doesn't look like Willi is going to be adopted after all!" Willi Whizkas thought he'd go and find Tushtots, since his former friend looked like being his only chance of staying in the area if his humans really were moving away.

He spotted Tushtots immediately, sitting upstairs in a bedroom window, but as soon as Willi Whizkas started walking towards the house, Tushtots turned his back on him. Willi Whizkas felt utterly dejected. "How could I have been so stupid and selfish?" He wept. He'd let things get out of hand with his best pal, and there didn't seem to be anything he could do about it. Even a plague of mice galloping across the garden would not have cheered him up. He trudged back to his own garden and decided to make another check to see if the removal van had arrived yet.

Something had arrived, but it wasn't the removal van. It was a large silver car, from which an important-looking couple emerged before walking up to Willi's front door, where Willi's humans greeted them warmly. Willi Whizkas didn't normally like strange humans, but he followed them in through the front door anyway. The humans introduced each other, then began going from room to room looking at everything very intently. When they all finally came down the stairs Willi Whizkas was sitting on the back of the sofa, so the lady came over and gave him a stroke

"You're a nice cat, do you come with the house?"

"You're more than welcome to him," the male human responded, "he's called Willi Whizkas, he's always getting up to mischief, he's been to the vets so many times he's got a season ticket!!" The strangers shook hands with Willi's humans and left, but over the next few days the house was gradually transformed. Large empty boxes arrived, which of course Willi Whizkas had to jump inside. One of his humans dropped a ping-pong ball in a box and he spent a mad ten minutes chasing it round and round until he was exhausted. He was then tipped out and the box was filled with objects wrapped up in old newspapers. Willi Whizkas went to see Gordon to explain what was happening.

"That's it then," Gordon informed him, "you're moving Willi."

Willi Whizkas resigned himself to his fate, since it was abundantly clear that he wasn't going to be adopted. He'd even asked Gordon, who told him that his old lady couldn't cope with another cat, especially as she had the bird in the cage to look after. Willi Whizkas left Gordon's house more sad than ever, especially as Gordon had pointed out that if the humans were packing things away then the move would be any day soon.

"It's time to say your good-byes Willi, you should do the rounds and see everybody you've got to know since you were a kitten." After a restless night, he decided to take some advice for once in his life, so he set about visiting all his old pals. His first visit was to Stinker of the Yard. Stinker wasn't half the cat he used to be, having doubled in size from overeating and under-exercising, and his fur was turning grey around his muzzle. But he was pleased to see Willi Whizkas and thanked him for calling, smiling at the memory of Willi spraying Sergeant Fang in his cage, the time the fairground was in town. Willi Whizkas laughed too, and told Stinker that spraying had become his party piece! The next call was on Hagar, an old friend of the family who had known him as a little kitten. He assured Willi Whizkas that he'd soon make new friends and have lots of adventures in his new home. Willi Whizkas was beginning to feel a little better by the time he got to Thugsby's house, in fact he felt almost chirpy! He looked across the road and saw the hamsters still in the bedroom window, running round and round the exercise wheel.

"Haven't caught it yet Thugs?"

"No!" Thugsby stated the obvious, "but I'm working on it." He wished Willi Whizkas all the best and bon voyage. Willi Whizkas thought that he would give the alley cats and the haunted house a miss as he didn't feel safe going there on his own, so that just left Ginger Tompkins, Gordon, Britney Kitney, and his best friend, Tushtots. Willi Whizkas got an unexpected thank you from Gordon for eating his breakfast leftovers, as the old lady he lived with would not put fresh meat down for him until the old crusty cat meat had all been eaten up, it just so happened that Gordon liked his cat meat to be fresh. Willi Whizkas felt used, but he didn't mind as he had enjoyed stealing the food as much as eating it! He went in to Gordon's house to have one last look at the bird in the cage, jumping up onto a sideboard to get a better view, but the parrot let out a deafening screech and Willi Whizkas shot straight out of Gordon's catflap, not stopping until he reached Ginger Tompkins' house. Ginger Tompkins was in his favourite spot on the wall overlooking Jacko's garden, with Britney Kitney sitting by his side. Willi Whizkas jumped up and sat between them.

"I'm not sure how long I've got before I leave," he panted, "so I've come to say a final farewell." Although he wouldn't admit it, Ginger Tompkins was very upset. Tushtots was too timid, Gordon was too old, and Britney Kitney too young for the sort of adventures he and Willi Whizkas enjoyed.

"If I don't see Tushtots again you both must promise me that you'll give him my apologies, tell him I really am very, very sorry about the way things have turned out, and even sorrier that I'm not able to see him to say good-bye properly." Willi Whizkas said humbly. "I'll have one last look, see if I can find him," with that Willi Whizkas was gone. Tushtots's catflap was still firmly locked, so Willi Whizkas walked all round his house, but there was no sign of Tushtots. Willi felt awful, what if he moved before he had time to say how sorry the was? He had to make it up to Tushtots. Then Willi Whizkas heard the clatter of a knife on his cat meat saucer beckoning him in for supper so he bounded back to his own kitchen.

It was a trap. He was bundled into his cat basket and securely strapped in.

"There you are Willi," his human said, "I hope you've said all your good-byes," his basket was placed in the back of the car on top of some old boxes. As they pulled away he caught a last glimpse of Gordon sitting in his window looking down at him. Ginger Tompkins and Britney Kitney were sitting on the wall, the little girl and Archibald had come into the street to wave him good-bye. But one thing was missing, and that was Willi's good-bye to his best friend, Tushtots. He realised that he would never, ever see Tushtots again, for once he sat down quietly in his basket without mewing, and sadly watched the world go by with tears in his eyes, as his little heart felt like it would break.